# FOLK TALES OF WALES

MAP SHOWING LOCALITIES OF THE STORIES

# FOLK TALES OF WALES

EIRWEN JONES

*Drawings by A. E. Bestall*

*First published by Thomas Nelson & Sons Ltd., November 1947*
*Reprinted 1949, 1950, 1951, 1953, 1955, 1957, 1959, 1961, 1964*
*New edition by Gomer Press, March 1978*
*Reprinted 1996, 2000*

ISBN 85088 473 X

## PREFACE

*The Folk Tales of Wales* goes into yet another edition, this time from the Gomer Press, Llandysul in the heart of Wales.

A book, like an individual, derives much of its life and inspiration from its friends. During the past thirty years, these have been very many, of all ages and from all parts of the world.

Indeed, the story behind the little volume is a happy folk tale in itself!

## CONTENTS

# 1 THE CROCK OF GOLD

" COME and play ! Gwyn, come and play ! " called the children of Llangybi to the merry boy who lived at the mill in the valley.

But Gwyn did not follow them to the river-bank. He climbed the mountain-side alone. The children thought he had gone to gather flowers, but Gwyn was searching in the grass for more of the strange brass coins he had found two days before.

" They are fairy coins ! " Gwyn's mother had said, when he showed them to her. " We will put them on the fire. No good will come to us if we hoard them."

Gwyn had been disappointed. He would like to have kept the coins with their strange designs.

" Promise me, Gwyn," she had said, " that if you see the elfin people you will not play with them." Gwyn had promised.

He remembered his promise now as he climbed the hill. He hung his head in shame. He knew that he had come that way in search of the little fairy folk. Would he find them ? Scarcely had he taken another step when he saw a little elf, dressed in green, with a buttercup set jauntily on his head. The little man did not speak but beckoned with his hand. Gwyn followed where he led the way down a long dark tunnel. Turning around Gwyn saw a clump of moss growing at the entrance.

For two years nothing more was heard of Gwyn.

"A beautiful sunrise," said Gwyn's mother, as she opened the door early one summer morning. "It will be a fine day."

"Hullo, mother!" Gwyn was seated on the doorstep. He ran forward and kissed her.

"Gwyn has come back! Gwyn has come back!" his mother called excitedly.

The miller ran to the door and gathered Gwyn in his arms.

"He hasn't changed the tiniest bit in all these years," they cried. "Never, never will we let him out of our sight again. Where have you been all this time?" they asked when Gwyn had eaten his breakfast.

"All this time?" echoed Gwyn. "Why, have I been away long? It was only yesterday that I went away from the children to climb the hillside."

"Not yesterday, little son," said the miller gently. "You have been away for a long time."

"Yes. I—I went through a long, long tunnel after the elfin messenger," began Gwyn. He grew silent, trying to remember the things that had happened to him, but try as he would the memories of his frolics in Elfin Land escaped him.

"Never mind, Gwyn," his mother comforted him. "The important thing is that you are back."

Yet Gwyn continued to puzzle. "See, mother. They gave me beautiful clothes when I left them." He opened his bundle and took out trousers of green satin and a jerkin of russet and gold.

His parents looked at each other.

"If he wears those clothes he will disappear again," said the miller.

"If that is so, we must not let him have the chance of wearing them," said his wife. She poked the fire into a blaze, placed the fairy bundle on it, and set it alight. "That, I trust, is the end of that," she said.

But the burning of the clothes did not end Gwyn's adventures with the elves.

Some time later the miller's family grew very poor. Ships laden with corn had been lost in the Irish Sea, and the mill became silent and empty.

"We are very poor, my dear wife," said the miller one night as they sat before their small fire.

"It is not your fault, my dear Ifan," answered his wife. "We must think of something that will help us in our need."

"There is the treasure of Pentyrch," said the miller, and he laughed.

"What is that, father?" asked Gwyn, who had been listening quietly.

"It is nothing, little son—just a folk tale. You know the great crag at Pentyrch beyond Llangybi? They say that a crock of gold has been buried beneath it."

"Let us try to get it, father," cried Gwyn, jumping up with excitement.

"It would be a foolish quest, little son." The miller shook his head and began to think of other things.

But Gwyn persisted: "Do try, father, do try."

The mother was preparing their scanty supper. She smiled at Gwyn's faith in the old folk tale.

"Promise the child, Ifan. You will be none the worse for trying."

"I'll be none the worse, but I'll be none the

3

better either." The miller smiled sadly. " But I will promise. It will be something for Shon and Lewis to do to-morrow. I have no work for them at the mill."

Gwyn rose early the next morning to go with his father and the men to the great crag at Pentyrch. Three of the strongest horses went with them, and the men carried great coils of rope.

As they passed through Llangybi, men asked whither they were going. They told their errand. The miller had many friends in the district, and they were all sorry for the misfortune that had befallen the little family. When the miller reached the crag, it was to find that all the horses of the neighbourhood had been brought there to help in the task of removing the great rock.

" Heave away ! Heave away ! " cried the men.

" You can heave away till daybreak," snarled a cruel man who was an enemy of the miller. " Nothing will move that crag."

" Yes, it will. Oh, I know it will ! " Gwyn clenched his fists in anger at the man's words. He must do something to help his parents in their distress !

He ran away from the crag towards the place where he had been playing when he entered Elfin Land. A group of elves were dancing there, but they stopped when they saw Gwyn and beckoned to him.

" I cannot come with you to-day," Gwyn explained breathlessly, " but I wish you would help me."

" What can we do ? " they asked.

" Can you help me to get some money ? My

4

parents are very poor, and we have not enough food," Gwyn explained.

"We will help you all we can," said the elves, and they began to dance and sing.

"But please help me *now*," cried Gwyn, growing impatient at the delay.

The Elfin King came near to him. He held out his sceptre and spoke with authority.

"There is a great crock full of gold awaiting you under the mighty crag of Pentyrch."

"Yes, yes, I know," said Gwyn. Tears filled his eyes. Was this all the help the elves could give him? "We have been trying there, but— but, although all the horses of the parish have been helping to pull, nothing will remove the great rock."

"I know that," said the King. Then he looked at Gwyn and asked very quietly, "Have *you* tried to remove the crag?"

Gwyn shook his head.

"Go back," commanded the King. "I command you to push the stone—alone. You shall see what will happen."

Gwyn thanked him and raced back to the Pentyrch crag even more quickly than he had raced to the hillside.

"Father, mother, listen!" he cried, and he told them what the Elfin King had ordered him to do. The miller and his wife shook their heads and smiled. Yet they were in such distress that the miller said:

"Very well, little son. You may try."

The people drew aside and Gwyn made his way alone to the great rock. He placed his small hand

He placed his small hand on the rock and pushed

on it and pushed. The crag rocked and then rolled headlong downward to the dingle below.

In the hollow where it had rested was a crock full of gold. Gwyn claimed it. The miller and his wife were rich for the rest of their lives, and when Gwyn was grown up, enjoying the good things of life, he did not forget his village friends—nor the little elfin folk who had brought him his good fortune.

## MIGILDI MAGILDI

Ffeind a difyr ydyw gweled
    Migildi Magildi hei now now ;
Drws yr efail yn agored
    Migildi Magildi hei now now ;
A'r Gôf bach a'i wyneb pur-ddu
    Migildi Magildi hei now now ;
Yn yr efail yn prysur chwythu
    Migildi Magildi hei now now.

## 2   MULE'S EARS

MARCH was the overlord of Lleyn. He had a great
fortress at Castellmarch, and he owned acres and
acres of fertile lands. Hundreds of servants called
him master, and he possessed horses, cattle, sheep,
pigs, and falcons. His oxen were so famous that
King Arthur himself sent to March to buy a yoke
for his own use. So rich was March that he pre-
sented a herd of oxen to the Great King.

March sat in his room in Castellmarch. Before
him were coffers filled with gold and precious
stones. But March looked sad. Despite his wealth
he was not a happy man. March nursed a secret
grief within his mind, and he feared night and day
that it would be revealed. This was the secret :
March had ears like a mule !

No-one knew this save the barber who cut
March's hair. When Bifan was appointed to be
March's barber, the overlord called him aside
and said :

" You must swear an oath that you will tell no

living creature of my misfortune. If you break that oath, either purposely or by accident, I swear that I will cut your head off."

Bifan promised that he would keep secret the fact that March had ears like a mule. As time went by Bifan the barber grew very unhappy. At first he grew as unhappy as March. Then he grew even more unhappy, for his was the more evil plight. Bifan spoke to himself and said :

" If March reveals the secret he will suffer shame, a very sorry thing to endure. If I reveal the secret I will suffer death, a sorrier thing to endure."

Day and night Bifan brooded on the secret. He lost his appetite, and grew pale and wan.

" I will call a doctor to attend to you," said his wife.

" No," pleaded Bifan, but the doctor came. He looked at Bifan's tongue and felt his pulse.

" There is nothing wrong with your body, my good barber," he said ; " something plagues your mind. Is it not so ? "

Bifan nodded his head, but he was afraid to open his mouth lest he should breathe one word of the awful secret.

" Take my advice, Bifan," said the doctor, as he clapped the barber on the shoulder, " tell your secret to someone. Confide this thought to your wife, else you will soon be dead."

Bifan tried to smile in answer. When the doctor had left the room he shuddered. Tell the secret to his wife, Mallt ? " 'Twere better that I proclaim the secret from the housetops," he cried bitterly.

Bifan walked along the shore, and then he

walked over the hill. If only he were rid of the awful secret! But he thought of what would befall him if he told the secret to anyone. Sadly he rubbed his neck to see if his head was still attached to his shoulders. He strode down to the village. He would take the risk and tell the secret to the doctor.

"What brings you here?" asked the doctor impatiently. "I am a busy man, and have no time to waste on your foolishness."

"The secret—" Bifan began.

"If it's that precious secret," said the doctor angrily, "go far away and tell it to the earth. The earth will keep faith with you, and will reveal your secret to no man."

He hastened away. Bifan stood thinking over what the doctor had advised.

"It is good advice," he said at length. "I will climb to the loneliest part of the hill and I will whisper the secret to the earth."

This Bifan did. Immediately he was happier. He returned home, recovered his appetite, grew rosy and fat, and was so kind and considerate to Mallt his wife that she went round the countryside declaring that Dr. Prydderch was a very able man.

Bifan had whispered the secret to the earth. There, in the darkness, he had not seen the reeds growing. He did not give the matter another thought. He had told his secret and was now a happy man.

March was preparing a great feast to welcome the other overlords of Wales to Castellmarch. He

9

had many minstrels, but in honour of his guests he sent to Gwynedd to borrow from Prince Maelgwyn, the piper Enoc. So renowned was Enoc's skill that he had played his pipe in the courts of all the kings of Europe.

Enoc set out for the Castellmarch in answer to March's invitation. The piper carried his pipe and played it as he walked across the hills.

" I will get me a new pipe," said Enoc. Seeing some reeds growing on the hillside, he cut himself a new pipe on the hillock where Bifan had knelt to tell his secret to the earth.

" A fine pipe ! " exclaimed Enoc. " This is the finest pipe I have ever possessed. It will play the sweetest music. I will not play it until I play before the guests at the feast."

When the guests had eaten March gave an order that Enoc should ascend the dais and entertain all the guests in the great hall with his music. Enoc raised his new pipe to his lips. Great was the astonishment of all within the banqueting hall when there came from the pipe not sweet music but the words :

" March has mule's ears ! March has mule's ears ! March has mule's ears ! "

March rose in anger, and unsheathed his sword.

" I will kill thee, thou mad piper ! " he cried.

" Mercy, sire ! " begged Enoc.

The courtiers intervened. Enoc recovered his breath, and pleading on his knees said :

" My lord, it is not my fault. I have tried to play the usual music on this pipe. The pipe must be bewitched. It will utter nothing but the words, ' March has mule's ears.' "

" Give me the pipe," said March. The hall was hushed, and in the silence March blew. " March has mule's ears ! March has mule's ears ! " uttered the pipe.

Slowly and fearfully Bifan made his way to the dais and told the king how the reed-pipe had come to learn the secret.

" I will pardon the barber and the piper," said March sadly. " The secret is now told."

But his shame was forgotten in the applause that rang to the rafters :

" March is ever merciful ! March is ever merciful ! "

## 3  TWTTI GLYN HEC

THE wicked sprites of the Mawddwy Valley molested the rich and the poor. In a small glen in Montgomeryshire there lived a poor widow woman named Mari and her baby, Robert.

Mari kept a cow. This cow she took to market, and having sold it for a goodly sum she returned home to the little cottage in the glen.

" Ah," said Mari, when she had counted out the money over and over again, " I am still a very poor woman, but this money will help me very much."

Robert was too small to understand, but he chuckled in his cradle as though saying he agreed. Mari beamed with pleasure.

" Yes, *cariad bach*," she said, " your mother will hide these gold pieces in an old stocking safe,

safe, safe within the chimney. I will use the gold to pay the rent. If there is any over I will buy a new gown for thee."

Robert chuckled yet again. Mari, having hidden the gold coins within the chimney wall, picked up the baby and carried him into the garden. Before she went to bed Mari determined to count the coins again, to make sure that they were all there. To her dismay she found that the nook where she had hidden her treasure was empty.

" No-one could have stolen it," she cried. " I have not left the house since I returned."

She ran from room to room, but could find no trace of the treasure. In great distress she ran to the outhouses. More misfortune awaited her there. She found that the two calves had been stolen. Crying very bitterly, she ran into the garden only to find that the poultry and the bees had also disappeared.

" Who can have done it ? " Mari wailed, rocking herself in the low stool on her hearth. " I have harmed no-one. Who is this who vents his anger on me, a poor widow woman ? "

She had expected no answer to her cry, and was therefore all the more amazed when there came a sharp knocking at her door. Who could be there ? All Mari's neighbours entered without knocking, so sure were they of Mari's welcome. Before Mari reached the door the knock was repeated.

It was growing dark, but Mari could see her visitor quite plainly. She was tall and very, very old, leaning on a stick. She wore a long green cloak lined with red. The hood of the cloak was thrown back, and the woman wore a tall black hat.

"Why are you crying?" asked the strange woman in a high-pitched voice.

"I have lost my treasures," cried Mari, and she explained what had happened since her return to the cottage.

The old woman placed a wrinkled hand on Mari's shoulder.

"Take comfort, my young woman," she said. "Take comfort, for I have much gold. I will pay your rent and give you enough money to buy four new calves as well as far more bees and poultry than you have lost."

Mari looked at the old lady in surprise. She did not look as though she were rich enough to buy all the things she had promised. The old lady must have read Mari's thoughts. From an inner pocket of her great cloak she took a great leather purse. This she opened and poured upon the small table a heap of golden coins.

"Oh!" cried Mari, clasping her hands. "I have never seen so much gold before!"

The old lady's sharp eyes were watching Mari keenly.

"I will give you all this gold if you will give me what I ask," she said in a hoarse whisper.

"I will give you whatever you ask," cried Mari, delighted at the thought that she would be able to pay her rent and restock her little farm.

She watched the gold coins glisten in the fire-light. Little did she think what the old lady was about to request.

"I am old, but not unreasonable," said Mari's

visitor. " I like to give freely. I give much, but always ask for little. For all this gold, then, give me this little child, lying here in his cradle."

Mari sank down on a stool, overcome by the old lady's words. She saw now that she was a witch, and she understood at once that it was the wicked sprites of the Mawddwy Valley that had stolen away her treasures.

" Oh no ! " Mari rose in alarm when she saw the old lady approach Robert's cradle. " Oh no ! I cannot let you have my baby."

Then she remembered how very poor she was, and seeing the great pile of gold upon the table she begged the witch to take any other thing from her cottage in return for it.

" No," said the witch angrily. " In return for the gold you must give me your baby. But I have told you I am not unreasonable. I will give you time to think. Besides, there is a law forbidding us witches to take our reward in less than three days."

Mari looked up in fear. The witch picked up her stick and prepared to go.

" I will return the day after to-morrow. If you still want the gold you know my bargain. You have one chance, however, of gaining possession of the gold without giving up your baby. If you discover my name the gold is yours."

She gathered up the gold, replaced it in her purse, and seated on her broomstick flew up the valley.

Mari gathered baby Robert into her arms. " No, no, my darling," she cried, " you are more precious than all the gold in the world."

When Robert was safely asleep in his cradle again Mari sat down before the fire. She was afraid to go to bed lest the witch might return and steal the baby, and the thought of her misfortunes kept her from sleep.

The next day she set out early for Llanbrynmair. She left Robert in the care of a village girl, having given her orders to keep careful watch over the baby and not let him out of her sight.

When she reached her journey's end Mari called on her relations, and explained to them the tragedy that had befallen her. They were very sorry to hear Mari's sad tale, but when she asked them to help they could only shake their heads and say : " Alas ! the wicked sprites of Mawddwy have molested us also ! "

Sad at heart, Mari began her homeward journey. Her way lay through a great wood, and she was anxious to pass it before night came on. She was half-way through a glade, and the light was darkening when she saw a sight so strange that she hid behind a tree to watch. In the small clearing the fairies were dancing. They were dressed like flowers—roses and buttercups, primroses, poppies, pansies—a host of fair colours. How Mari wished that Robert was there to see them !

Suddenly a witch appeared, dressed in a green and red cloak and bearing a stick. When she saw the fairies dancing she too tried to dance. Mari put her hand to her mouth. She had almost laughed aloud at the way the old witch hobbled around, pretending she was a fairy.

The fairies saw the witch. They huddled together in terror, and then scattered in all directions to hide themselves in the trees of the wood.

The old witch continued to dance alone, and as now there was no fairy music she sang to herself in a cracked voice. Mari crept nearer to listen to the words of the song. She listened carefully and made out the witch's words :

> The sprites of Glen Mawddwy
> Will wring my old neck
> If the widow discovers
> I'm Twtti Glyn Hec.

Mari clenched her fists in excitement. She almost cried out. Then fear crept into her mind —had she heard aright ? She listened again. The witch was hobbling around, repeating the jingle. Mari left her to her frolics and crept cautiously out of the wood. Once on the high road she ran homeward. Robert was safe. Mari danced around him in glee.

"To-morrow, my darling," she cried, "something strange will happen."

And Robert chuckled, as he always did, to show that he agreed.

The next day the old lady came as she had promised. She was dressed in green and red, and carried her stick as she had done before. She came into Mari's kitchen and emptied her bag of gold on the small round table.

"You may have all the gold if you give me the baby." She crept nearer the cradle to look at Robert as he lay sleeping. "Or," she glanced back over her shoulder, "if you can tell me my name."

Mari sighed deeply.

" How many times may I guess ? " she asked sadly.

" As many times as you like." The old witch laughed, feeling quite sure that she had won little Robert.

Mari sat on her little stool. Her head was buried in her hands. She pretended to think. Then she called out name after name :

" Ceinwen, Nesta, Dillwen, Rhona, Shani, Gwenno."

The witch only shook her head each time. Mari got up and walked to the centre of the room.

" I will try just once again," she said.

" Try away," cackled the witch unheedingly.

There was a silence.

" Your name is Twtti Glyn Hec," called Mari.

There was a wild scream. It seemed as though a great wind hurled round the small kitchen, and in the draught the old witch flew up the chimney. The sprites of Glen Mawddwy went rushing after her.

Mari gathered up the gold coins heaped upon her table. With them she paid her rent, and bought new calves and poultry and bees. Nor did she forget a new gown for Robert.

From that time Mari lived happily. The sprites of Glen Mawddwy molested her no more ; indeed, as time went on they proved to be her greatest friends.

## HEFO DEIO I DYWYN

Mi dderbyniais bwt o lythyr
   Tra la la la la la la la.   Tra la la
Oddiwrth Dafydd Jones o'r Brithdir ;
   Tra la la la la la la la.   Tra la la
Ac yn hwnnw 'roedd yn gofyn
   Tra la la la la, tra la la la
Awn i hefo Deio i Dywyn
   Tra la la la la la, tra la la la la
   Tra la la la la la la la la.   Tra la la.

## 4  GARETH'S DANCE

THERE are pleasant pastures in the Vale of Llangollen, and there Gareth liked to graze his master's
sheep.

One evening while Gareth was driving the sheep
back to their fold he amused himself in playing
his flute. When he reached the wood at the foot
of Dinas Bran he stopped suddenly. Before him
on the roadway stood a little man. He wore a
pointed cap and a jerkin of brown, his trousers
were of green moss, and in his hand he carried
a fiddle.

In his amazement Gareth dropped his flute on
the road, but the little man raised his fiddle and
continued to play the tune that Gareth had been
whistling.

"I wish you good-evening," said the little man,
bowing with a flourish.

"I wish you the same," whispered Gareth
through dry lips.

The little man saw that the shepherd boy was afraid, so he tried to console him, saying :

" My fine lad, you need not be afraid of a man so small as I. Tell me, do you like to dance ? "

" Yes," said Gareth.

He was afraid to say more to the merry dwarf,

" I wish you good-evening "

but he dearly liked to dance. The little man came very close to Gareth and stood on tiptoe.

" Stop a moment," he called, " and I will show you the finest dancing there is to be seen."

Gareth turned the flock aside into a field near by. When he had done so the little man beckoned him to return. The light had faded, and in the after-glow of sunset Gareth saw hundreds and hundreds of fairies approaching. They were

19

dressed as flowers, in many colours. Each fairy carried a blazing torch, and in passing Gareth each fairy curtseyed.

He acknowledged their greeting, and taking off his cap he bowed with a flourish as he had seen the little man do when he had greeted him. The dwarf by this time had seated himself on an old tree-stump, and had raised his fiddle in readiness to play. The fairies began to dance, and the dwarf played a merry tune.

Gareth longed to join in the dance. He hesitated. Had he not heard that evil things befell those who danced with the fairies on the hill?

"Come and dance, Gareth," called the little man, pausing for breath.

Gareth took one backward glance at the flock of sheep. They were all safe and quiet. There could be no harm in joining in *one* dance. He would drive the flock home after he had finished.

"Yes, I will dance," Gareth called to the little musician. "Play on, merry fiddler."

As soon as Gareth had finished speaking everything changed. The fairies changed into weird-looking animals the like of which Gareth had never seen before. Yet the strangest thing of all was the change that came over the little fiddler.

His cap fell off, leaving his ugly face in view. Two horns grew out of his head. His feet were changed into hooves, and he had a long tail. His face and hands were blacker than soot, and his eyes shone like red-hot coals.

When the evil fiddler began to play, Gareth began to dance, nor could he stop, though he called and called on the musician to break the spell by playing another tune. All through the night Gareth danced, and the gaunt and hungry animals danced around him. In vain Gareth called for mercy. When the sun had climbed high into the heavens he was still dancing.

When the master found that Gareth had not brought the sheep down from the hill he went out in search of him, fearing that some accident had happened. He was all the more annoyed, therefore, to find Gareth dancing wildly in the wood near Dinas Bran.

" O master! master! " cried Gareth, " stop me! Stop me! "

" Stop yourself," growled the farmer. " Enough of this foolish nonsense."

" O stop me, master! " begged Gareth.

" In the name of Heaven, what can the matter be? " asked the farmer.

No sooner had he said those words than Gareth stopped dancing and fell down as though dead. The little fiddler disappeared, and with him went the stricken animals, but Gareth's flock of sheep remained safe and secure in the wood.

Gareth recovered from his faint, but though he often tried hard to do so, he could never fully explain the strange adventure that had befallen him.

My name's Gareth Morgan, I live at Llangollen,
   The vale of St. David, the flow'r of North Wales;
My father and mother, too, live in Llangollen,
   Good truth I was born in the sweetest of vales.
Yes, indeed, and all countries so foreign and beautiful
   That little valley I prize far above.
For indeed in my heart I do love that Llangollen,
   And sweet Jenny Jones, too, in truth I do love.

## 5 THE FAIRY HARP

IN the caves on Cader Idris there lived many fairies. They were friendly little people, and often went into the villages to visit the country folk. The fairies were welcomed in most of the cottages, and in return for the kindnesses they received the little folk would bring many gifts. But evil would befall those who were unkind to them. Yet unkind people were very few in the valleys round Cader Idris.

Tudor ap Rhys sat alone in his cottage, for his wife had gone to visit her friends in Dolgelly. He watched the smoke curl out of his pipe as he sat thinking of the past. He felt lonely, and kept looking at the clock, watching for the time when Anna would return.

Tudor began to sing, at first quietly, for Anna had often laughed at his efforts. Then he sang more loudly, for the singing broke his loneliness. He began another tune.

"Why does Anna laugh when I sing?" he asked himself. "I can sing quite bravely."

He sang an old folk-song, and his notes were true and sweet. When he had finished there was a knocking at the door.

"Come in," called Tudor. But no-one entered. The knocking was repeated.

"Come in!" called Tudor, more sharply this time. "Doors are made to come through, so please enter."

He rose from his armchair on the hearth in order

to open the door, but before he reached it three travellers came in. Tudor saw at once that they were travel-stained and weary, and even before they spoke to him he felt sure they had walked over the hill-paths of Cader Idris. What he did not realize was that they were not three ordinary travellers; not for a moment did he think that they were three of the fairy-folk come to test the welcome Tudor ap Rhys gave in his cottage.

The three travellers were shy in crossing the threshold. One of them stepped forward and addressed Tudor.

" Sir," he said, " we are very weary after our travels, but all we ask of you is a little food to sustain us, so that we may continue our journey."

" Dragon wings ! " Tudor swore. " A little food ? Is that all you need ? What a pity Anna is not home, we could then have had a true feast ! "

The men laid their coats aside.

" Come to the table," Tudor invited. " You are welcome to all that is here. Bread and cheese. Will that do, sirs ? I have eaten my supper, and left so little, but let me look in the cupboard."

The travellers began to eat. Tudor returned.

" Here, my friends, take it all. Anna's cake is well worth a healthy bite, and people have come from far to taste her fruit tart."

Tudor heaped before his guests all the good things he could find.

" You are hungry, good friends," he said. " Eat and satisfy yourselves. We give the best welcome we can at the home of Tudor ap Rhys."

The travellers ate silently. Then one of them spoke :

" Sir, when we came to your door we heard some sweet singing."

Tudor bowed his head in modesty. How Anna would have laughed if she had heard !

" I was amusing myself," he explained. " I only sang to pass the time."

" Sing again," said the three travellers together.

" Anna's cake is well worth a healthy bite "

Tudor sang song after song while they finished their supper. The men rose from the table and prepared to leave. The man who had first spoken addressed their host :

" Sir, we thank you. Since you have been so generous, we wish to repay you. It is in our power to grant you whatsoever you wish. Tell us what you desire."

" Well," began Tudor, " I am pleased to give

24

you a welcome. I ask no reward. It would have been well if Anna were here—she would have prepared you a feast."

"Tell us what you want," said the travellers together, "for we must continue our journey."

"I would like," said Tudor slowly, "a little harp—a little harp that could sing and play sweet music however badly my clumsy fingers would pluck the strings. But, good friends, take no notice of my wish. It is a foolish request."

"Not at all," said one of the men. "Surely that is not foolish."

He pointed to the hearth behind Tudor. Tudor turned. On the hearth he saw a beautiful golden harp set with jewels.

He raised his hands in amazement. "It is the most beautiful harp I have ever seen!" he cried. He looked towards his guests, but they had disappeared.

Tudor plucked the strings of the harp that had come to him in such a strange way. He smiled.

"I'll play a merry tune," he said. "I'll surprise Anna when she returns."

25

He plucked the golden strings, and the harp played sweet music. The tune was merry and sprightly, and delighted Tudor's heart. Tune after tune he played. He could not leave the fairy harp, such sweet music did it play.

There was the sound of footsteps. Anna was returning accompanied by some friends. Tudor began to play the music of a fairy dance. Before Anna had time to speak in greeting she began to dance, and her companions joined in the frolic. Round and round the kitchen they tripped, while Tudor played more merrily on his golden harp. Only when he ceased to play could the dancers stop. Tudor told them how the wonderful harp had come into his possession.

The news spread through the countryside: Tudor ap Rhys had come into possession of a fairy harp having strange powers! People came from far away to see the fairy gift.

" Play the harp, Tudor," the visitors begged.

When he played, those who heard felt bound to dance.

" Stop playing, stop playing, Tudor ! " the dancers would cry. " We have no breath left to dance any more, and our limbs are aching."

Tudor played sometimes mercifully, sometimes mercilessly, to show the power of the magic harp. The visitors would return to their homes to recount wonderful stories of Tudor's gift.

One day there came to the cottage a man who was Tudor's enemy. He had come to mock. Tudor was no musician, he declared. Where had the poor cottager learned to play a golden harp ?

Tudor invited him into the house. Very courteously he spoke to the visitor, though he remembered how often he had suffered his insults in silence.

" Let me hear you play," scoffed the man.

Tudor began to play the golden harp. To the man's annoyance he could not help dancing. It was now Tudor's turn to laugh.

" Stop ! " cried the man.

But Tudor continued to play a very merry tune. Tudor played and the man danced. Tudor laughed and the man cried. Tudor laughed till the tears ran down his cheeks. The man twirled round and round, calling on the musician to stop, till Tudor's sides ached with laughing. Then he felt it was time to stop. He set the harp aside, and the man sank down on the floor, unable to dance one step more.

When the visitor had gone Tudor turned to the harp to play yet one more tune. He plucked the strings, but the harp was silent.

" Fairy music was not meant to be played in spite," said a sweet voice. Tudor looked round the cottage but could see no-one.

Sad at heart Tudor failed to sleep that night. He rose early in the morning to examine his silent harp, but to his dismay the fairy gift had disappeared.

" It is all my own fault," said Tudor to Anna, who stood sorrowfully beside him. " If ever I have a fairy harp again I'll be more careful how I use it."

But though Tudor lived to be a very old man he never received another fairy gift.

# 6  THE ANCIENTS

" WHERE will I get me a wife ? " called the Eagle, as he clung to a rugged crag on the Stackpole Rock in Pembroke.

His sharp eyes looked far out to sea, where a dolphin frolicked in the great waves. But the Eagle paid no heed to the dolphin.

" Alack and alas ! my mate has died," he moaned to the wind that beat and blustered round his lonely perch. " Who is worthy to replace her ? I am the king of the birds. Where will I get me a wife ? "

" Marry the Owl," answered the South-west Wind. " Marry the Owl who lives in the little dell in the Valley of the Tâf."

The Eagle blinked his eyes and thought. " You advise me well, O South-west Wind. But as I am king of the birds it were well that I make enquiries about the Owl. Is she worthy to be queen ? Is she old and is she good ? "

The South-west Wind did not stay to speak further to the lordly Eagle, but sped away towards the Precelly Hills, bearing rain-clouds to quench the thirst of the parched lands.

The Eagle said : " I will go to the park lands of Menevia. I will ask my friend the Deer all about the Owl of the Tâf."

Soaring high into the sky he glided down again slowly and gracefully. He then summoned the Deer to a lonely nook where he bade him tell all about Mistress Owl.

The Deer, rubbing his antlers against the bark of an old Welsh oak, said : " Behold this old oak, O king of the birds ?  I am old—so old that I can remember this oak when it was only an acorn on the very old oak yonder.  Seven hundred years it has taken this oak to grow into a great tree. For seven hundred years it has flowered in its glory.  For seven hundred years it has been dying.  So old is it, O king, that I advise you to ask of the oak the age of Mistress Owl of the Tâf."

The Eagle turned to the oak and asked his question.  The oak rustled its leaves nervously when addressed by the king of the birds, but answered clearly :

" O king, I have known Mistress Owl many hundreds of years, so many hundreds that I lose count of them.  Mistress Owl was old when first I knew her.  I am old, it is true, but my friend the Salmon of Roch is older than I.  He may help you.  Go, sire, and ask him the age of Mistress Owl."

The Eagle flew to Roch and asked his question. The Salmon basked in a sunny pool, and was quite indifferent to the Eagle's impatience.  Yet he answered straightforwardly, saying :

" Go to the Blackbird of Rudbaxton.  He is older than I.  He will know the age of Mistress Owl.  Go, ask him."

The Blackbird stopped whistling his merry tune when he saw the Eagle approach.  He hid in fear in the shadow of a great flint.

" Have no fear, happy warbler," called the Eagle.  " I come but to ask the age of Mistress Owl of the Tâf."

The Blackbird, ruffling his feathers, forgot his nervousness.

"O mighty king," he whistled, "you see this old flint that casts its shadow on the land? I can remember it when it was far greater. In my childhood it was a high and rugged mountain. Each night before I go to rest I have rubbed my beak upon it. Thus has the towering mountain become but a great rock. Know then that I am old, very old, but even I cannot remember Mistress Owl but as she is to-day."

The Eagle's face puckered in thought. The Blackbird was sorry for him. "I have a friend who is far older than I, O king. If you will fly to the Toad of Freystrop, he may be able to tell you something about Mistress Owl."

The Eagle bowed his thanks and flew to Freystrop. The Toad was resting in a muddy pool, but he hopped on to a tuft of heather and answered the Eagle:

"Sire, I eat the dust, to be sure. Yet I do not eat enough to satisfy my hunger. Around the bog you see great hills. I can remember this land a great plain. I am old, very old. You can reckon my age when I tell you that it is *I* who have eaten away the land between the great hills of the Precelly range. Yet, old as I am, I can only remember Mistress Owl as a very old woman, screaming, 'Tu-whit! Tu-whit! Tu-whoo-oo-oo!' just as she does to-day."

The Eagle thanked the Toad. He flew straight away to the Tâf Valley. He was satisfied now that Mistress Owl came of a good family, and that she was old, very old.

The Eagle and Mistress Owl were married. The wedding guests were the Deer of Menevia, the Salmon of Roch, the Blackbird of Rudbaxton, and the Toad of Freystrop—all old, very old, but the happy couple loved them all the more because of that.

## 7  Y GLOMEN

'Fel roeddwn i ryw fore hawddgar
   Yng nghwr y coed ac wrth fy mhlesar
Ar frig y pren, mi glywn ryw glomen
Yn cwyno'n glâf " Aw ! beth a wnaf
   Am f'anwyl gymar ? "

A nesu wnes yn nes i wrando
   Beth oedd y gangen ferch yn cwyno ;
   A mentro wnes a gofyn iddi
" Y lana o liw, a'r fwyna'n fyw
   Beth yw dy g'ledi ? "

" Rhyw g'ledi mawr sydd yn fy mynwes
Wrth gofio'r cur a'r poen a gefais ;
Wrth gofio'r mab a'r geiriau mwynion
   I'm calon rhoes drwm glefyd loes—
   Fe dŷr fy nghalon."

Y Glomen fwyn, O paid a chwyno
   Fe gyfyd haul ar fronnydd eto
A phan y dêl, daw'r coed i ddeilio—
   Ti gofio'n dda, pan ddelo'r ha'
Daw'r gweilch i rodio.

## 8   THE FAIRY SALVE

An old couple named Huw and Bet journeyed to Aberystwyth to hire a maid at the mid-winter fair. When they arrived at the hiring-place they found many servants to choose from.

" See the girl who is standing alone near that doorway ? " exclaimed Bet to her husband. " She is the one I like."

" Let us speak to her then," said Huw, always anxious to please his wife. " If we can pay the wage she asks, we will take her home."

The old couple spoke to the young girl, who agreed to work for them. She told them her name was Elin. The three lived happily in the homestead in the shadow of the sheltering hills. In the long winter evenings Elin and her mistress would sit weaving while Huw sang and recited to the strumming of his harp.

When summer came and the evenings were long and light, Elin no longer stayed in the kitchen. She took her spinning-wheel to the stream in the meadow and there she worked and sang.

The fairies came and helped her to spin, but Elin said nothing of this at home lest her helpers should be displeased. Huw and Bet knew nothing of the fairies' work, but when they saw all the wool Elin had spun, one would look at the other and cry :

" We have indeed been fortunate in hiring so good a maid as Elin."

Winter came, and Elin helped her mistress to weave during the long evenings. Spring came and Elin was with them no more.

"It was too good to last," said Huw sorrowfully.

"What can have happened to our good Elin?"
Bet sobbed. "Have the fairies taken her?"

The answer was yes, though Bet did not know
it at that time. Later she was to discover the
strange fate that had befallen Elin.

One stormy winter's night Bet was sitting alone
in the farmhouse when someone knocked at the
door. Bet bade her visitor enter. A tall man,
out of breath with running, came in and asked
Bet to go with him over the hillside.

"Why?" asked Bet in astonishment.

"I need your help," exclaimed the man, "and
there are others too who need your help."

Bet was the most generous of women. When
she heard that someone needed her help she
threw her cloak over her shoulders, paused only
to raise the hood over her head, and bowing in
the face of the storm, followed the stranger up
the hill.

Bet had known the paths from childhood, but
on this particular evening she seemed to be following a new one. She kept close beside her companion, and followed him into a great cavern in
the side of the hill. At the far end of the cave
was a lofty doorway. The man, after pausing to
unlock the heavy studded door, stood aside for
Bet to enter.

When her eyes had grown familiar with the light,
Bet saw that she was in a spacious room with
splendid furnishings. There was a four-poster
bed with golden curtains. On it lay a beautiful
lady and her little baby.

" Take care of them," said the man, and Bet ministered to the two who needed her help.

" This will be your room," said the man, opening the door of a smaller room.

Bet entered. The table was laid, and there was all manner of good food upon it. In her room she found all the things that she needed. She was all the more surprised, for she could see no servants or anyone who could have prepared for her wants.

" I do not understand," muttered Bet to herself. " Perhaps I am growing old—but in truth I do not understand."

One morning the man came to Bet and said :

" In future when you bath the little baby, place some of this salve on his eyes. Be very careful you do not put any on your own eyes. Should you do so, evil will befall you."

" I will take care, sir," said Bet.

For several days Bet was very careful. She rubbed the salve over the baby's eyes, and at once washed her hands. " Evil will befall me if it reaches my eyes," Bet reminded herself each day.

One day Bet had bathed the baby and placed the salve on his eyes. Suddenly her left eye began to itch. Without thinking of the evil that might befall her, Bet raised her hand to soothe her eye. But there was some salve upon her fingers, and so a strange thing happened, for now though she saw everything as she had seen it before with her right eye, she saw things altogether differently with her left eye.

To her right eye the room appeared as beautiful and luxurious as before. To her left eye it appeared as a damp miserable cave, unfit to live in. Bet

looked round, and where the four-poster bed had
stood with its beautiful hangings she saw a clump
of ferns and bracken.  Bet stepped forward and
looked more closely at the baby and the young
woman who lay upon the bed.

"Elin !" cried Bet.  "My dear, dear maid.  Is
it here that I find you ? "

Before Elin could answer, Bet could see with
her left eye that they were not alone.  There were
many servants, maids, and pages moving about
the cave, as light in their movements as the passing of dandelion tufts.

"Mistress !  Mistress ! " cried Elin.  "Yes, it
is I, Elin.  But tell me, how is it that you know
me ? "

Bet told how she had by accident rubbed the
salve into her eye.

"We must be careful," said Elin in a whisper,
"that my husband does not get to know of it."

"So that strange man is your husband ! "
Bet exclaimed.  She did not know whether she
was glad or sorry at Elin's news.

"I will tell you all about it this evening, when
he is safely away."

For Bet the hours dragged slowly by.  She was
impatient to hear Elin's tale.

"This is my story," said Elin.  "You and the
master were pleased when I could spin and weave
so well.  You did not know that the fairy-folk
helped me.  They helped me freely on one condition—that I should marry their king."  Elin
paused as though she were thinking deeply.  "I
promised," she continued, "for I wanted their
help, but "—and here she laughed—" I had no

35

intention of keeping that promise. To make sure
that they would not worry me to keep it, I always
carried with me a knife, sharp and keen. They
were afraid of the sight of that knife.

"I feared that they might carry me away when
I was sleeping. To save myself, each night I used
to lay a branch of the mountain ash across the
foot of my bed. For months and months I was
safe from them—so safe that I grew careless. One
evening, very tired, I crept into bed, having forgotten to place the mountain ash at my feet.
I woke in the land of the fairies—but hush!
Here comes my husband."

In his presence Bet was very careful not to show
that she could see differently with her left eye.

Time passed.

"Good-bye, mistress! Good-bye!" sobbed
Elin one evening. "He will take you away in
the morning. I shall not see you again."

At sunrise the man beckoned to Bet. He gave
her a bag of gold, and led her home by the path
she had come. Great was the surprise of Huw,
and many were the questions he asked, but there
were many, many things Bet could not explain.

"We must go to the mid-winter fair at Aberystwyth," said Huw some months later. "We
must hire a maid to take Elin's place."

When they reached the town Bet saw her sister
busy bargaining at a stall.

"The fairy folk are here to-day right enough,"
said Nance. "Did you ever see such a crowd?
Prices too are right high. Good for those who
are selling."

The fairy-folk were there as Nance had guessed, but no-one saw them but Bet. She saw them clearly with her left eye. Near by she saw a stall of flannel. A man was stealing a roll of cloth from it.

" Nay ! nay ! do not be dishonest," cried Bet. She ran forward and saw that the man was Elin's husband.

Overcome with surprise, Bet forgot Elin's warning not to show she could see magic things with her left eye.

" How is Elin ? " asked Bet, all excitement. " How are Elin and the little baby ? "

" They are well—quite well," the man answered. " But tell me which eye you see me with."

" With this one," said honest Bet, pointing to her left eye.

Immediately the man struck her left eye with a plantain flower, and the eye became dead and useless. For the rest of her life Bet could only use her right eye.

" It will serve me as well as two," she said, comforting herself.

Throughout the rest of her life Bet searched carefully with her right eye, but never again did she see Elin or her little baby.

Pwsi Meri Mew
Ble collaist ti dy flew ?
Wrth fynd i lwyn tew
Ar yr eira mawr a'r rhew.
Pa groeso gest ti yno
Beth gefaist yn dy ben ?
Ces fara haidd du coliog
A llaeth y gaseg wen.

# 9  GELERT

PRINCE LLEWELYN had a dog called Gelert. It had been given him as a gift by his father-in-law, and from the first the prince and the dog were firm friends. In the hunt there was no dog so brave and fearless as Gelert. Yet within Llewelyn's palace no dog was so gentle and affectionate.

One fine morning in early autumn Prince Llewelyn was going hunting. The huntsman blew his horn in the castle courtyard. Knights and pages, horses and hounds crowded before the castle walls. Llewelyn walked into the midst of the hounds.

" Don and Juno, Seren and Morwen are here," he cried, and continued to count the dogs. " But —but where is Gelert ? "

The huntsman blew his horn again at the prince's command, but no Gelert answered the call.

" Strange that Gelert does not hear the horn," said Llewelyn sadly, as the huntsmen moved away.

Llewelyn did not enjoy his ride that day. When evening came he was glad to ride back to his castle. As he rode through the gateway Gelert sprang forward to greet him.

" Gelert ! Gelert ! Where hast thou been hiding all day ? "

Llewelyn leapt from his horse to pat the dog, but he drew back shuddering, for Gelert's jaws were dripping with blood.

The prince spoke in anger. Gelert cowered against the wall in fear. Llewelyn strode into his castle in search of his little son. The little prince was often left in Gelert's charge, and Llewelyn feared the dog had done some harm. He leapt up the stone staircase, his spurs ringing at every stride, and ran into his little son's room, Gelert padding after him.

In the doorway Llewelyn paused. He saw that the walls and floor were covered with bloodstains.

In the doorway Llewelyn paused

The child's cradle had been overturned. The baby prince was nowhere to be seen.

"Little son!" Llewelyn called, but there was no answering cry.

He raised the broken cradle, but the child was not beneath it. He searched round the room, but failed to find a trace of the young prince. Llewelyn saw Gelert standing near.

39

"Thou hast done it!" he cried. "Thou evil dog!"

Beside himself in his distress, Llewelyn drew his sword and thrust it up to the hilt into the dog's body. Gelert moaning, and looking sadly at Llewelyn, sank down on the floor and died. Llewelyn cried out in sorrow as he saw the dog die. The prince's cry was answered by another cry, faint but loud enough to reach a father's ear. In two strides Llewelyn was at a couch in the far corner of the room.

There, safely hidden, he found his young son, just awakened from a sweet sleep. Behind the couch lay the body of a wolf, newly slain.

"Alas, brave Gelert!" cried Prince Llewelyn, "too late do I discover thy brave deed. But for thee, my baby son would have been devoured by this fierce wolf. How grievously have I repaid thee!"

Llewelyn mourned deeply. His courtiers tried to comfort him.

"It is useless thus to lament," said one. "You cannot make the dead dog alive again."

Llewelyn thought what he could best do to preserve the memory of his brave dog. Gelert was buried. A great grave was dug and a monument was placed over the body. Llewelyn hung there his horn and sceptre as a tribute of respect. The grave can be seen to-day at the place called the grave of Gelert—Bedd Gelert.

## 10  LLEWELYN AND HIS DOG

THE spearman heard the bugle sound,
　　And cheerily smiled the morn,
And many a brach and many a hound
　　Attend Llewelyn's horn ;

And still he blew a louder blast,
　　And gave a louder cheer,—
" Come, Gelert ! why art thou the last
　　Llewelyn's horn to hear ?

" Oh, where does faithful Gelert roam ?
　　The flower of all his race !
So true, so brave !—a lamb at home,
　　A lion in the chase ! "

That day Llewelyn little loved
　　The chase of hart or hare,
And scant and small the booty proved,—
　　For Gelert was not there.

Unpleased, Llewelyn homeward hied ;
　　When, near the portal seat,
His truant Gelert he espied.
　　Bounding his lord to greet.

But when he gained the castle door,
　　Aghast the chieftain stood ;
The hound was smeared with drops of gore,
　　His lips and fangs ran blood !

Llewelyn gazed with wild surprise—
    Unused such looks to meet,
His favourite checked his joyful guise,
    And crouched and licked his feet.

Onward in haste Llewelyn passed
    (And on went Gelert too),
And still, where'er his eyes were cast,
    Fresh blood-drops shocked his view !

O'erturned his infant's bed he found !
    The blood-stained cover rent,
And all around the walls and ground
    With recent blood besprent !

He called his child, no voice replied !
    He searched, with terror wild ;
Blood ! blood he found on every side !
    But nowhere found the child !

" Monster ! by thee my child's devoured ! "
    The frantic father cried ;
And to the hilt his vengeful sword
    He plunged in Gelert's side !

His suppliant, as to earth he fell,
    No pity could impart ;
But still his Gelert's dying yell
    Passed heavy o'er his heart.

Aroused by Gelert's dying yell,
    Some slumberer wakened nigh ;
What words the parent's joy can tell
    To hear his infant's cry !

Concealed beneath a mangled heap
   His hurried search had missed,
All glowing from his rosy sleep,
   His cherub boy he kissed !

Nor scratch had he, nor harm, nor dread ;
   But the same couch beneath
Lay a great wolf, all torn and dead,
   Tremendous still in death !

Ah, what was then Llewelyn's pain !
   For now the truth was clear :
The gallant hound the wolf had slain,
   To save Llewelyn's heir.

Vain, vain was all Llewelyn's woe :
   " Best of thy kind, adieu !
The frantic deed which laid thee low
   This heart shall ever rue."

And now a gallant tomb they raise,
   With costly sculpture decked ;
And marbles storied with his praise,
   Poor Gelert's bones protect.

Here never could the spearman pass,
   Or forester, unmoved :
Here oft the tear-besprinkled grass
   Llewelyn's sorrow proved.

And here he hung his horn and spear :
   And oft, as evening fell,
In fancy's piercing sounds would hear
   Poor Gelert's dying yell.

LONG, long ago the people of Anglesey were frightened by a great storm. For days they remained hidden in their homes, afraid to go out because of the high wind and the thunder and the lightning.

When the gale had passed far out to sea and when the thunder was but a distant rumble, the people came out on the cliffs to discover what harm the great storm had done. To their astonishment everything was much as it had been before. The people laughed joyously, but an old, old man stepped forward and said in a quavering voice :

" Take care ! I warn you all. Storms never come alone. They always leave something behind."

As though in answer to his words a little boy called from the edge of the cliff :

" Look ! What is that out to sea ? "

The people looked and saw a boat approaching the island.

" It is a strange boat," a man cried. " See, it has no sail or oars."

Those standing behind him shaded their eyes and looked out to sea.

" Take care ! " warned the old man who had first spoken. " You know what manner of people travel in boats without sails or oars."

Those around him came nearer, hoping he would advise and help them. The old man continued :

" People who travel in such boats are wicked

" See, it has no sail or oars "

people. They have been bound in chains, and placed in the ship by men who live in distant lands, and then turned adrift on the sea. They belong to no land, but the demons claim them for their own.''

The people of Anglesey did not wait to hear more. They rushed down to the beach to drive away the demon ship, but when they reached the shore the ship was at anchor, and the men and women had landed.

The strange people took no notice of the people of Anglesey. They spoke an unknown language, and so it was very difficult for the two peoples to understand each other.

" We will leave them alone," said the men of Anglesey. " provided they do not harm us ; they can build their huts on that rocky strip of land. We need pay no heed to them. They will go away again in the next storm."

" Take care ! " the old man cackled. " Do not forget they are demons."

Weeks went by. The demon people lived on their strip of land and kept to themselves. The men were smugglers, often venturing far away on their evil expeditions. They seldom came near the island people. The demon women sometimes came to spy on the villagers and to tell their fortunes.

As long as the demon people left them alone the villagers allowed them to remain on the coast. Later, however, the demons took to thieving, and the people of Anglesey decided it was time to drive away their unwelcome guests.

They armed themselves with weapons and went

down to the shore, determined to drive the demons out to sea.

" Take care ! " warned the old, old man. But they paid no heed to him, so anxious were they to be rid of these evil visitors.

When the islanders were ready for attack the demon people lined up on their strip of land, and took from their pockets big handkerchiefs. The islanders thought that they were going to wave them in farewell.

" Take care ! " warned the old man, who had followed them.

From each handkerchief came a swarm of black insects, which attacked the islanders, blinding them and stinging them so that they were glad to go back to the safety of their homes. After that the islanders left the demon people alone, suffering their evil spells patiently, fearing that if they attacked again worse evil would befall them.

On the mountain-side lived a young farmer named Tudor. His grandmother had been known as the Wise Woman, for she had power over good and evil spirits. The grandmother was now dead, and Tudor lived alone in the farmhouse. One evening Tudor had returned from the village and was sitting alone in the kitchen, thinking of the harm that the demon people had done in the valley.

" Something must be done," said Tudor to himself, " and I am the one to do it. Did not my wise old grandmother say that no evil spirit could curse me, for I have a birthmark in the shape of a cross on my right arm ? "

He sat and thought what plan he could best follow.

" I *must* do something," he said aloud, and then, as though in answer, came the echo of the old man's words, " Take care ! "

But Tudor laughed at the words scornfully. " I am the one who must break the evil spells," he said. " I am the one who must save the island people."

He rose from the hearth and went down the valley to the church. He went to his grandmother's grave, and filled his pockets with loose earth. Returning to his farmhouse, he scattered the soil in each room, and then placed a little in each of the outhouses.

" That will save me from the curses of the demon people," he said. " But I must hurry ; there is more to do."

From the stable he took some old and rusty horseshoes. These he fastened to the doors of the house and barns. From his small front garden he gathered bunches of marigolds. He filled some vases with the flowers, crossed himself and prayed, " Holy Mary, protect me."

Then he went down the lane that ran in the direction of the shore where the demons lived. Passing one of his fields he saw a strange sight. The cattle, instead of lying down, drowsily chewing their cud, were seated on their haunches, catfashion, and from their horns blazed flames of fire.

Tudor hesitated. Should he go on down to the demon village, or break the demon spell here at his farm ? Quietly, but very quickly, he ran back to the farmhouse and fetched his gun. He returned to the lane that led to the field where the cattle were seated.

He stood still, amazed by a strange sight. The cattle were seated as he had left them, but now some hares were there also. Each hare was milking a cow. Tudor stared at the hare nearest him. There was something familiar about its face.

"Nance the Witch," said Tudor under his breath. He raised his gun and fired.

There was a cloud of smoke. When it had cleared, Tudor saw the hares leap across the lane and scurry in headlong flight towards the steep cliff where the demons lived.

Tudor paused only to comfort the frightened cattle, and then hurried to the demon settlement. He made straight for the cottage of Nance the Witch. Before he entered he could hear loud wailing. Seated before her fire was Nance, with a great wound in her side.

"They have sailed away and left me. They have gone—all gone away," she wailed.

When she saw that it was Tudor who had entered her cottage she was very angry, but Tudor, remembering all her evil deeds, took no notice of her and her curses. Had he not protected himself before he set out?

"You will not change yourself into a hare again, Witch Nance," he said.

The witch tottered to her feet and said, "I curse you! I curse you! May you fall down and break your neck."

But Tudor only laughed.

"Here is your broom, Witch Nance," he said.

" The best thing you can do is to sail away again over the sea to your companions."

He strode back to his farm on the mountainside, whistling a merry tune. That night, when he was about to go to bed, he remembered the witch's curse.

" Better make sure," he said. He went out in the moonlight and searched in a small wood until he found a branch of mountain ash. On his threshold he stopped and stuck a number of pins into the twig.

There was a sharp cry. Nance the Witch appeared before him.

" You are torturing me ! " she cried. " Take those pins away ! I am in pain."

Tudor looked at her and spoke very calmly :

" I will take the pins away if you promise to take yourself away over the sea on your broomhandle."

Nance saw that it was useless to argue. She promised.

Tudor removed the pins. Nance disappeared, and from that day the people of Anglesey saw no more of her or of the demon people.

## 12  THE BRECON ELVES

ON the side of the hills known as the Brecon Beacons lived some merry elves. They were happy, busy little folk, always ready to help human beings.

A poor old shepherd lived on the hillside. One

morning he returned to his little hut after being busy in the sheep-fold all night. He found his kitchen clean and tidy and a nice breakfast prepared. He wondered who could have come there to help him, since his hut was a lonely one, many miles away from the nearest farm.

Hearing a sweet voice singing, he turned and saw a little elf dancing. The little elf looked so small and poor that the shepherd said :

" Come, seat yourself by my cosy fire. I will get you some breakfast."

The elf did not answer, but sat on the fender as the shepherd had bidden. When he was given food he ate it, bowed his thanks, and disappeared. The shepherd thought for a moment, and then said to himself :

" It was that little elf who cleaned my house and prepared my breakfast. How I wish I had money to repay him ! "

He had hardly finished speaking when he felt a sharp pain under the sole of his right foot.

" There must be a stone in my shoe," he said. He unlaced it and took it off. Within the shoe he found a gold coin. Each morning after that, when he put on his shoe he found in it a gold coin.

The shepherd told the people of the neighbourhood about the strange happening. After that everyone was anxious to do something for the elfin people, hoping that in some way they too would receive a rich reward.

Non was the wife of Morgan, the farmer at Cwm. She was kind and loving to everyone. One day she saw an elfin lady carrying a little baby. They looked so poor that Non was very sorry for them.

" Come into the house," said Non. " I will give you some food." But the elfin lady shook her head. " Stay a moment," said Non. " I will give you a little woollen shawl to wrap round the baby."

She ran into the house and returned. The elfin lady took the shawl, tore it into small shreds and let them blow away in the wind. Then picking up her baby, she stamped her tiny foot and said, " Non, you have insulted the Queen of the elves. We shall pay you out for this." She thought that Non was being kind and helpful only so as to gain a reward. In this she was misjudging Non, who was generous and kind by nature, and who was always doing her utmost to help those in distress.

Non hurried back to the house, weeping. Morgan, her husband, tried to comfort her.

" I did not know she was the queen of the elves," cried Non. " She seemed to think that I was just anxious to receive a fairy reward. I only meant to help her. Now all the elves will curse us."

" I don't think there is any need to worry," said Morgan soothingly. " I expect they will forget all about us. Cwm is far away from everywhere."

But the elves did *not* forget about the farm at Cwm. It seemed as though all the elves had come there to do as much mischief as they could. They upset the milk-churns, they led the cows astray ; they stole the horses' shoes and drove the sheep far down into the valley. They broke the crockery, stole the farming tools, removed the furniture, hid the clothes and locked the doors, so that it became difficult for Morgan and his family to continue to live at Cwm.

The old cowman at the farm said to Morgan: "Take my advice, master. Go and see the witch on the Beacon. She's an old hag, but if you pay her, she will tell you how to be rid of the evil little people."

Morgan looked at Non. "What shall I do?" he asked.

"I do not like your going to the witch on the Beacon," answered Non, "but we must do something. We cannot go on like this."

"I will come with you," said the cowman. "I'm not afeard of the Beacon witch."

His words decided Morgan's move. So one day, when it was very cold, the two men climbed to the top of the highest Beacon.

"She isn't here!" said the cowman disappointedly.

There was a loud wailing sound. The Beacon witch was travelling towards them at terrifying speed on her broom-handle. She alighted at some distance from the two men. Catching sight of them, she sat down upon a sheep's back, and the frightened animal scurried towards them.

The witch listened to the men's complaint. "I'll rid you of the evil elves," she cackled. "I've a bone to pick with them this long day."

She stroked her long nose, thinking out a remedy. "Go back," she said. "Pack up all your belongings. You must pretend that you are leaving Cwm. Go down by the longest paths as far as Pont-Neath-Vaughan. Cross the bridge. Then you can turn back. You will have deceived

53

the elves. They will think that you have gone to live in another part of the country."

The men returned to Cwm and told Non all that they had been advised to do. The witch's advice was carried out. The furniture was heaped on carts, the sheep and cattle were herded together, and Morgan, heading the procession, led the way down into the next valley.

On the bridge at Pont-Neath-Vaughan Morgan stopped to speak to an old friend.

" Ah ! Morgan, you are leaving the farm on the side of the Brecon Beacon ? " he said in surprise.

" Yes ! Yes ! We are leaving. We are going to live in the next valley," little voices chorussed together before Morgan had time to answer. Morgan turned. Elves were crowded in every nook and cranny of the furniture. They were huddled together between the horses' ears. They were swinging from the wheels of the carts. They were trailing behind with the dogs and the sheep.

Non raised her hands in dismay. She was too disappointed to speak.

The cowman broke the silence : " The Beacon Witch has deceived us. Her spell has failed."

" Let us turn back," said Morgan. They all returned to Cwm.

The elves were more mischievous than ever. Morgan and Non suffered their tricks without complaining until the elves stole the baby for three days, carrying her away and hiding her in a nook on the mountain-side.

" We must try again," said Non, " to see if

there is a way by which we can make our peace with the elves."

A new vicar had come to live in the neighbourhood. He was an old friend of Morgan's.

" I will walk down to the church this evening. Perhaps Ifan can advise me."

It was the time of the hay harvest. Non came out into the farm-garth. She called in a loud voice, " Morgan, how many men are expected to help in the harvest to-day ? "

She spoke clearly. She knew that the elves were listening.

"There will be twenty extra men," called Morgan.

" I will prepare a feast in readiness," answered Non.

Non and the maid busied themselves in the farm kitchen. They prepared the table, setting places for the extra twenty men.

" We must roast a frog for the feast," called Non clearly to the maid. " If we boil a handful of daisy petals they will serve as vegetables."

She looked around the room. A group of elves were seated on the mantelpiece. They stopped swinging their legs when they heard Non's strange words. They had been looking forward to a chance to steal the good food from the table before the men arrived to eat it.

" We can put the food in thimbles," Non said, following the maid out of the room. In the doorway she stood hidden behind a curtain. She peeped out and listened.

The elves were clustering together, speaking shrilly, quickly :

" Did you ever hear the like ? "

" Daisy petals for food ! "

" A frog as a feast for twenty and more ! "

" We can't put up with this ! "

" Surely, we shall starve ! "

" *Must* we stay here ? "

They chattered together, each taking no heed of what the other was saying. One elf got up and balanced himself on the fender rail.

" Why should we stay ? " he called. " We will go. We know our way far off to the bridge of Pont-Neath-Vaughan. We will cross the river and go to the rich farms in the valleys beyond. Who will come with me ? "

The elves clustered around him, each declaring that he was ready to come.

Non hid more deeply in the folds of the curtain as the army of elves marched past her. When the tramp of tiny footsteps had died away Non picked up the baby and carried her out into the hayfield.

" Morgan ! Morgan ! they are gone ! " she called happily.

Morgan tossed the baby into the hay. " They won't come back again," he said.

And time proved that he was right.

> Y Cobler du bach at yr esgid,
> Y Cobler du mwy at y last,
> Y Cobler du mawr at y fotas,
>   Fe'i gwasgodd hi rhyngddo a'i frest.
>   O la la la la la la la la
> O'r anwyl y rheiny ar unwaith
>     Ho ! Ho !
> Pob un yno'n canmol ei waith.

BENLLI was the Prince of Powys, rich in lands and cattle.

One frosty morning he was hunting. The horse galloped into the woodland, and there Benlli saw a beautiful maiden. He called to her, but she only waved her hand in answer and disappeared.

" She is a beautiful maiden ! " cried Benlli. " Who can she be ? "

He rode on, hunting the wild boar. But Benlli's mind was not on the chase.

" I love that beautiful maiden," said Benlli. " I love my wife no longer. She has grown so old and ugly."

Twice again he saw the lovely maiden. Each time he called, but she did not answer. Then one evening, as deep in thought he paced the paths of the forest, the maiden appeared before him.

" Do not run away, my fair one," begged Benlli. " Stay with me and live in my beautiful palace."

The maiden smiled.

" Before I come," she said, " you must send away your wife. Then I will marry you. But there is one condition. I belong to the fairy world. One evening each week I must be free to return to Fairyland. You must not follow me. If you keep to this condition I shall never grow old. I shall remain young and beautiful until the gorse bushes grow in the hall of your palace."

" I promise everything," said Prince Benlli.

They returned to the prince's palace. They found that the prince's wife had disappeared.

"My name is Morwen of the Woodlands," said the beautiful maiden, when the courtiers came to honour her.

For many years Benlli and Morwen were very happy. Each week Morwen disappeared on a visit to her home in Fairyland. Then as time went on, Benlli began to wonder why she still went on visiting her home. He grew discontented and feared that his wife was under some evil spell.

One day Benlli gave a great feast to celebrate his victory in war, and to his castle came the chief men of the realm. Among the most honoured guests was a monk named Wylan, who sat beside Benlli on the dais, in sight of all the guests. Benlli did not know that Wylan was a magician.

"Prince Benlli has some secret grief," muttered Wylan to himself. As they walked in the palace gardens Wylan said, "Oh, Prince Benlli, you have many blessings, yet tell me why you are so sad."

Benlli told the monk how Morwen disappeared mysteriously each week.

"Your greatest need is peace of mind. I will give you peace of mind, but in return you must promise to give the woodland maiden to me, and also a gift of money each year to the monastery yonder."

Benlli thought for a while. "I agree," he said to Wylan, and he returned to the palace.

That night Wylan hid his book of sorcery within the folds of his gown, and made his way along a winding path to the great stones blocking the entrance of a cave that led to the land of the fairies. There Wylan sat and watched.

He heard a rustling of leaves and the sound of silken skirts. He looked up from his book and saw Morwen of the Woodlands hasten past. Wylan watched her until she was lost to sight in the dark-

He saw Morwen of the Woodlands hasten past

ness of the cave. He began to chant his incantations, the wind carrying his words across the moorland.

" May Prince Benlli be at peace ! " he called as he fingered his learned book. " May he have peace, for he has promised a gift to the monks and a gift to me also. Morwen of the Woodlands is to be mine."

There was silence awhile. Then Wylan continued: "I take an oath that I will marry her in the chapel of the monastery. She must come to meet me there at dawn. I shall be there to greet her and marry her."

Having chanted these words over and over again he hastened towards the monastery. When he reached the cloisters he beheld a very tall lady seated on some steps of stone. There was something strange about her. Wylan stepped nearer. Now she seemed no longer strange but very familiar. On her hand he saw the ring with the precious rubies that Benlli had given to Morwen.

"Take me for your wife," she said. "I have become a giantess now, but you have taken an oath that you will marry me."

Wylan was silent.

"Seat yourself beside me," said the tall stranger, "and I will tell you all that has happened to me. I am ugly now. I am a giantess. Twenty-five years ago I was beautiful and fair. Then it was I first became Benlli's wife." She grew sad and thoughtful. She continued: "When I grew older, I lost my beauty. In losing my beauty I lost Benlli's love. Like you, Wylan, I studied sorcery. I spoke to the fairies and made a bargain with them. I promised to enter Fairyland for one night each week and become a giantess. In return the fairies promised to make me beautiful for the rest of the week."

Wylan stared at her in surprise. She went on speaking: "By making this bargain I once again, as a woodland maiden, won the love of Prince Benlli, for I and Morwen of the Woodlands are one and the same. I kept my vow to Benlli. I told him I would remain beautiful until the gorse bushes grew in the palace hall." She stood up and wrung her hands in anguish. "All was well," she said, "until someone chanted an evil spell against me, and now it has come about that I am bewitched as a giantess. But you have promised to marry me, so take me to the monastery chapel."

Wylan looked at the giantess, and he was filled with fear. He made the sign of the Cross.

"May you be restored to Benlli, Prince of Powys," he cried. "May peace be restored to me."

Morwen was restored to Benlli. He welcomed her with open arms, for in her he saw both his early wife and Morwen of the Woodlands. For a long time they lived happily in their castle. When they died their castle sank beneath the earth. The waters gathered over it, forming a lake—the Lake of Llynclys.

On a summer's day, if you row to the middle of the lake and peer down into the water you can see the castle deep down in the depths. Wylan's name remains in the name Croes Wylan and The Wylan. Throughout the district people tell the story of Morwen of the Woodlands.

Robin Goch ar ben y rhiniog
A'i ddwy aden fach anwydog ;
Ac yn dwedyd yn ysmala
" Mae hi'n o'er, fe ddaw yr eira."

Gwen lived in a lonely cottage on the moorlands beyond Llanwrtyd. She did not find her cottage lonely, for Gerallt, her little boy, amused her with his pretty ways. At evening time Prys, her husband, returned from his work as a woodman on the great estate near by.

Many elves and fairies lived on the moor. Gwen saw them dancing at night-time, bearing little will-o'-the-wisp lanterns that flickered through the heather.

" Take heed," said a gipsy woman at Gwen's door, " that the sprites do not steal away that pretty bairn of yours."

Gwen laughed. She had heard that fairies changed babies in their cradles, but Gerallt had outgrown his cradle by now. The fairies would not want to change him ! Then Gwen shuddered and drew her arms closer around her darling son.

One evening as she was preparing a meal in readiness for Prys she heard the horse stampede in the stable. What could be the matter ? Gwen ran out of the kitchen and into the stable. A few quiet words and more soothing strokes, and Noll was quiet again.

Hardly had she finished quietening the horse when she heard a great thud in the cowhouse. Gwen ran across the yard and opened the half-door. The cattle were lowing piteously. Gwen spoke to them soothingly as she had done to the horse. She left the cattle chewing their cud contentedly.

" Enough of these alarms," exclaimed Gwen as she was returning to the house. " And now for a quiet evening."

As she entered, Cariad, the terrier, barked strangely in the porch.

" Quiet, doggie," cried Gwen. " One would think all you creatures were bewitched this evening."

" M-mum-mummy," a thin little voice lisped from the kitchen settle.

Gwen ran to pick up Gerallt. She stooped, then hesitated. This was not her son ! Frantically she looked round the kitchen, but Gerallt was not to be seen. She opened the door of the grandfather clock, but he was not hidden inside. She ran upstairs in a vain search, and then returned to the kitchen.

" Mum-mummy," called the little child as he tottered uncertainly on his small legs.

At that moment Prys came in and greeted the child. Gwen ran to her husband and told him all that had happened.

" You are tired, my dear Gwen," Prys said kindly. " So tired are you that you are imagining things. We will prove if this is little Gerallt. Let me call the dog. He will play with the child if he is Gerallt."

" Cariad ! Cariad ! " Gwen called, and at the sound of her voice the terrier came scampering into the kitchen.

The terrier sniffed suspiciously at first, and then he played with the child as he had played before.

" That is proof enough," said Prys happily. He ate his meal, satisfied that all was well.

But Gwen kept watching the child carefully. She bathed him and put him to bed as gently as though he were Gerallt, but deep in her heart she felt quite sure that the child was not her son.

The next afternoon she left the child in the care of a young girl, and set out on a lonely path to a small cottage where a wizard lived.

The wise man listened to her tale. " I am sorry for you, my young woman," he said. " I will help you, and I will ask for no reward. Do exactly what I tell you, and you will have your son restored."

Gwen hastened home. She told Prys what the wizard had advised her to do.

" This child is ours, Gwen," said Prys patiently. He looked at Gwen's sorrowful face and added, " But if it pleases you, do what the wizard advises. It can at least do no harm."

The next day, when the sun was overhead, Gwen locked the doors of the cottage. She drew the blinds and shut out the light from every nook and cranny in the wall. She took an egg and, beating it in a basin, shell and all, placed it on the fender.

" Mum-mummy," called the little child, pointing at the basin. " What for ? "

" To drink, my dear," answered Gwen. She turned to the cupboard and pretended to look for a cup, but she listened carefully to the words the little child kept chanting :

> I am more old
> Than man can tell,
> Now shall I drink
> Wine and eggshell.

Gwen, pretending she had not heard, said nothing in reply. She undressed the child and put him in his cot to sleep.

The next day she visited the wizard again and told him what had happened.

" Good ! " cried the wizard, rubbing his hands with satisfaction. " Now you must find a white fowl with three black feathers on its head. Kill it with a silver knife, then roast it in its feathers before the fire. You will shut out the light as before, and you will watch the fowl as it roasts. Do not take your eyes off it until it has disappeared into nothingness."

Gwen hastened home to tell Prys what the wizard had advised. By this time Prys had begun to think Gwen was right, and that the child was not theirs.

Together they searched the countryside for a white fowl with three black feathers. At last they discovered such a fowl nine parishes away. They carried it back to their lonely cottage, and drawing the blinds, they roasted the fowl, watching it carefully till the last feather was burnt.

" Mum-mummy," called the little child from the settle, but never once did Gwen or Prys turn in answer to the cry.

When the last feather was burnt there was the sound of sweet music.

" Mummy ! Mummy ! " Gerallt called, and the sound of his voice was sweeter than the sweetest music.

He looked pale and frail but otherwise none the worse for his adventure with the mischievous fairies. Gwen ran to him, gathering him in her arms. Prys sang to him, and Gerallt crooned happily.

Never again did the elves steal him away.

> Bwrlwm, bwrlwm,
> Tatws yn berwi
> Dwr ar y tân
> I olchi'r llestri.
> Torti, torti,
> Bara gwyn yn llosgi
> Dwr ar y tân
> I olchi'r llestri.

## 15  RODERIC'S RETURN

RODERIC lived in a cottage near the church. One morning he set out to work in the great quarry high up on the hill. He stopped on the narrow path thither and listened to a bird singing.

"Is it a nightingale?" Roderic asked himself. "It is singing so sweetly that I will stop and listen."

Roderic sat down on a big stone. He looked at the little bird perched on the branch of a tree.

"It has finished its song," said Roderic. "Before I go to the quarry I will return to my house, and tell my neighbours of the wonderful bird."

He looked once more at the tree, but the bird had now flown. And as he looked he saw the branches and leaves of the tree shrivel and die. Roderic ran back to the village to tell of the strange event, going first to his own house.

"Where is the door?" Roderic cried in bewilderment when he reached home. He discovered it at length, but it was half hidden in ivy. Then he looked at the church, and saw that the tower had fallen in ruins. He turned to enter his house.

An old, old man stood in the porch.

"Who can this old man be?" thought Roderic. "He is so old that I am sure I have never seen him before."

Aloud Roderic said, "What are you doing here?"

"A strange question indeed," the old man said. "Who are you that you question what I am doing here in my own house?"

"*Your* house!" exclaimed Roderic angrily.

"Yes, *my* house," answered the old man, more angrily.

There was silence. Each glared at the other. Then the old man said to Roderic:

"Tell me your name."

"My name is Roderic."

"Ah! Roderic," the old man said, stroking his beard as though he were trying to remember something. "Roderic!" he said at length. "Ah, I have it. I have heard my great-grandfather speak of you on many occasions. He told me how his family had searched for you through the long years, and yet failed to find you. Arwyn, the Elder, said you had fallen under the spell of the fairies, and would not be free until the sycamore tree withered and died. Come into the old house," he cried, taking Roderic by the arm. " You are the great-grandfather of my great-grandfather. I am a kind of grandson to you, and you shall treat me as such."

Roderic stepped across the threshold, and the smile that lit up his face as he entered showed that he had returned to his home.

## YR HEN WR MWYN

Ble' buoch chwi neithiwr, yr hen wr mwyn.
   Yr hen wr mwyn mwyn mwyn mwyn
      mwyn mwyn mwyn
   Yr hen wr mwyna'n fyw ?
Bum yn pysgota, boys
    Flal di ri di rei do
    Flal diral- diri-do
    Flal di ri di rei do.

## 16   THE SQUIRE OF HENDY

MEN looked with envy at Madoc of Hendy, a squire of great wealth, owning rich pastures. He gave much to the poor, but men still envied him.

" He gives a little but keeps much," said one to another. " He could give much more. Madoc will be rich always. Nia, his wife, is a fairy."

Madoc heard their words although he pretended not to. He walked alone in his pastures and thought of Nia, his wife. He remembered how he had first seen her in the moonlight near the brook running through the meadows of Hendy.

" She is a good fairy," Madoc had cried. " See how the stars shine in her crown."

He ran after her. Over bog and waste land he ran. At length he caught her on a high crag.

" My beautiful fairy," cried Madoc, " return with me to Hendy—return and be my wife."

The fairy looked at him, and then she placed her hand in his and said :

" I will come, I will be your wife."

Madoc often blessed the day he had brought Nia home. He had grown rich and prosperous, and though he knew of the envy of his jealous neighbours, he was happy.

Now, as he walked the meadows Madoc was no longer content.

" Perhaps I have become too prosperous," he muttered. " Besides, I have grown tired of Nia. She is still beautiful, I know, but when I first saw her she was a fairy—now she is but a woman."

When he had finished speaking he heard sweet bells ringing. Turning he saw a fair maiden travelling in a golden coach. Her retainers were dressed in green and gold, and each was armed with a tiny sword. The little procession passed close to the place where Madoc was standing. He could not remove his gaze from the beautiful fairy.

" Oh ! " he cried, " I wish I had married that fair lady instead of Nia."

His heart was filled with bitterness. He followed the coach as quickly as he could. To his joy the horses were halted at a hillock near by. The fairy alighted. Madoc called, and she waved her hand in greeting. He ran to her, but to his dismay she ran from him. Madoc hastened after her. Down a dingle and across a dell he hurried, but the fairy fled before him. Over a brook and up a ravine she led the way. Madoc clambered after her.

"Wherever she goes I will follow," he declared. "I will catch her. This beautiful fairy shall be my wife."

When he had reached the top of the ravine Madoc quickened his footsteps. He knew his way over this part of the land, and at times he almost caught up with the fairy. Onward he hastened. He was now but a few paces from her. The fairy ran into a farmhouse. Madoc followed. He saw the fairy seat herself in an armchair at the fireside. He ran forward and touched her on the shoulder. She looked up. Madoc bowed his head in shame.

"Forgive me, my dear wife," he said. "I had to travel far to see that my wife Nia and the good fairy are one."

After this Madoc lived happily at Hendy until in later years Nia took her leave of him and returned to fairyland. Madoc spent his time alone. He grew unhappy and morose. The farm was neglected, and he could get no-one to help him in his work.

"I am plagued by a troll," cried Madoc bitterly, "a wicked fairy haunts me, and nothing but evil comes to Hendy now." He walked over his farm. "Behold," he cried, "my ricks have been set on fire, my barns are unroofed, my cattle are destroyed, and a disease attacks my crops. Surely a troll has cast a spell over my possessions. I will lie in wait for it and I will destroy it."

He wandered in search of the troll's home. "I am sure that the troll lives in the ravine beyond Hendy," Madoc cried. "To-night I will hide myself there, and when the troll appears I will attack."

So Madoc hid himself in the deep ravine. The night was dark, but Madoc saw the troll. With a fierce cry he rushed forward:

"I have got you! I will destroy you!"

He gripped the troll around the waist. It turned on him, grasping both his shoulders. They wrestled together, their shadows reflecting in the waters of the small lake beneath as they reeled and staggered together. Madoc took a deep breath for a final effort.

"I will overthrow you," he declared to the troll.

With a mighty effort he overthrew it, hurling it to the ground. Madoc stood over it, then knelt upon its chest and grasped it by the throat. He drew his sharp knife to kill it. The moon shone through the cloud-rack and Madoc paused. With a cry he threw the knife into the lake, for the face of the troll was his own.

Sorrowfully he made his way back to Hendy. Someone opened the door.

"Nia!" cried Madoc. "You have returned!"

Nia smiled and welcomed him.

"You have destroyed your passions, Madoc," she said. "When you killed the troll you extinguished your pride and your hate. Now it is possible for us to be truly happy as man and wife."

And the years that followed at Hendy showed that Nia was right.

MARGED was a poor old widow who lived on the banks of the river Mynach.

One afternoon in winter time when the daylight had faded early, Marged stood on the banks of the river. She watched the water swirl past her in high flood to fall over a great rock in the river bed.

Marged had watched the river flow in high flood before. Although she looked at the water her mind was elsewhere, for Marged was grieving for her cow:

> Old Marged Glandynach of Pontymynach
>  Had lost her only cow;
> Across the ravine Malen was seen
>  But to get it she could not tell how.

"Malen! Malen!" Marged cried, but the cow continued to nibble as though to say that sweeter grass grew on that side of the river.

"How you got there, indeed, I do not know. How I shall get you back is more than man can tell!" Marged paced the river bank. "Woe is me!" she exclaimed. "Whatever shall I do?"

Marged was speaking to herself, and not expecting any answer. Great was her surprise, therefore, when a voice cried from behind her:

"What is the matter, Marged?"

Marged turned in fear. She was glad to find that no evil spirit had spoken to her. Before her stood a man clothed in the gown and hood of a monk. Around his waist was a rosary, and as he spoke the man fingered the beads.

Marged had not heard him walk across the meadow, and she did not know where he had come from. She remembered, however, that she had been worrying about her cow, Malen.

"Woe is me!" cried Marged, glad to have an audience for her sorry tale. "Look there on the slope beyond the river, there is Malen, my only cow, and a beautiful cow she is, too. However am I to get her back? Woe is me! Woe is me!"

Marged buried her face in her apron and sobbed bitterly. The monk laid his hand upon her shoulder.

"My poor old woman," he said very gently, "do not worry any more. I will bring her back."

Marged showed her surprise in her face.

"How will you do that?" she asked.

"I will tell you," said the monk. "I have a hobby. It is to build bridges. If you wish, Marged, I will build a bridge over the falls for you."

"I wish you would," declared Marged excitedly, "but," and here she sighed deeply, "I am only a poor widow woman. I have very little money, and you are sure to ask a big price for building a bridge over these falls. Whatever shall I do?"

The monk looked at her curiously. "I never drive a hard bargain with the poor," he said. "Many say I am easy to please." He smiled and stroked his chin, pretending to think deeply. "I'll tell you what I'll do," he added. "I will build the bridge. To repay me, you shall give me the first thing that comes over the bridge. Do you agree?"

Marged agreed.

" Go home to your cottage," said the monk.
" I will build the bridge and call you when it is
ready. I won't keep you waiting long."

Marged obeyed the monk. Yet in passing him
on the footpath she saw there was something
strange about the holy man, for she could see the
shape of two horns standing up under his cowl.
His face was very dark—almost black, thought
Marged. His eyes shone like red-hot coals.

" He never drives a hard bargain, he said,"
Marged muttered to herself as she sat on her
hearth. " Why did he ask for the *first* thing
that comes across the bridge ? He means to
have my precious cow. He shall not have her."

Marged stamped her foot to show that she had
made up her mind that Malen should remain hers.
But how should she repay the monk ? Marged
sat and thought.

When the monk called on her to come to the
river falls Marged persuaded her small dog to
follow her.

" See, 'Smala, I have a crust for thee." Marged
threw a piece of bread on the path, and the little
dog leapt after it.

When Marged reached the river the monk
pointed to the fine bridge he had built. " Have
I not built it well over these steep and treacherous
falls ? " he asked.

Marged was slow in praising his handiwork.
" It *looks* a fine bridge," she said grudgingly, " but
is it a *strong* bridge ? Tell me."

" A strong bridge ? " exclaimed the monk
angrily. " Of course it is a strong bridge."

" I have my doubts," Marged said. " Do you think it is strong enough to bear the weight of this loaf of bread when I throw it on to the bridge?" She drew a small loaf from under her cloak and showed it to the stranger.

The monk laughed loud and long. " Will the bridge bear the weight of that loaf ? " he snarled. " Throw the loaf on to the bridge and you will see."

> In her pocket she fumbled, a crust out-tumbled,
>> She called her little black cur ;
> The crust over she threw, the dog after it flew,
>> Said she, " The dog's yours, crafty sir ! "

The monk was speechless. He had made the bargain to gain possession of Marged's cow.

" I do not want your dog," he snarled, " I have no use for him."

With that the monk, striking the ground three times with the hoof that served him for a foot, vanished in a cloud of smoke and flame.

" He was the Devil sure enough," cried Marged.

Then she called to Malen to come over the bridge. Marged drove the cow homeward, and 'Smala ran behind, wagging his tail with joy that he had not been made to follow the evil spirit that had built the Devil's Bridge.

## 18  Y SAITH RHYFEDDOD

Mi glywais ddwedyd echdoe'r boreu
*Chorus :*    Ta la ring ting ta la ring to
Fod llong o blwm yn nofio'r tywod ;
*Chorus :*    Ta la ring ting, ta la ring to.
A llong o goed yn myn'd i'r gwaelod
*Chorus :*    Ta la ring ti ring ta la ring to.
A dyna un o'r saith rhyfeddod.
*Chorus :*    Ring, ta la ring to.

Mi glywais ddwedyd fod y petris
Ar fin y traeth yn chwareu tennis ;
A'u bod yn gwneud eu peli o dywod
A dyna dau o'r saith rhyfeddod.

Mi glywais ddwedyd fod y cryman
Mewn cae o haidd yn medi ei hunan ;
A'i fod yn torri cefn mewn diwrnod
A dyna dri o'r saith rhyfeddod.

Mi glywais ddwedyd fod pysgodyn
Yn cadw ty mewn twmpath eithin ;
Ac yno'n byw ers pedwar diwrnod
A dyna bedwar o'r saith rhyfeddod.

Mi glywais ddwedyd fod y mochyn
Ar ben y car yn llwytho rhedyn ;
A'i fod yn gwneud ei lwyth yn barod
A dyna bump o'r saith rhyfeddod.

Mi glywais ddwedyd fod y ceiliog
Ar graig y Llan yn hela sgwarnog ;
A'i fod yn dala dwy mewn diwrnod
A dyna chwech o'r saith rhyfeddod.

Mi glywais ddwedyd fod y wennol,
Ar Fôr y Dê yn gosod pedol ;
A'i morthwyl aur a'i hengan arian
A dyna'r saith rhyfeddod allan.

## 19  THE BELLS OF ABERDOVEY

MANY centuries ago—in the sixth century to be
exact—the King of Ceredigion was Gwyddno. He
owned great wealth, and ruled over vast lands,
but none was more fruitful than that part called
Cantre'r Gwaelod.

More people lived in that district than in any
other part of Wales. Twenty fortified towns had
been built on it, and the busiest ports of Britain
were on its shore. Not only were they busy ports,
but they were very old ports, known to traders in
every part of the world. In the very early days
the Phœnicians visited them when they came to
our island in search of tin, calling our country
Bri-tin, the island of tin.

The greater part of Wales is high mountain

and moorland, but Cantre'r Gwaelod was very low-lying. It was below the level of the sea, and the men who lived near the coast had built a great dyke to stop the tide from flowing far in over the land.

"We will build watch-towers along the great dyke," the builders cried, "we will set guards in them, and they will warn us of any weakness or fall in the dyke. The guards will serve under Prince Seithennin, who lives close at hand in the port called Port Gwyddno."

Prince Seithennin was a mighty warrior. He had one great vice—he drank too much. He was known to be one of the three greatest drunkards of Britain.

The prince placed the guardianship of the dyke in the care of his steward, and the steward, busy with other matters, entrusted the care of the dyke to his assistant. Yet another prince had charge of the dyke at its far end, at Mochras near the hills of Ardudwy. He was called Teithrin, and he was an excellent guardian of the dyke.

Teithrin entrusted the care of the dyke to no-one but himself. One day he walked along, inspecting the dyke. He saw great gaps in it, and his mind was filled with alarm. He walked along until he came to that part of the dyke which was in the care of Seithennin.

"Come to my castle," Prince Seithennin greeted Teithrin. "Come, a feast is prepared."

Teithrin accepted the invitation to the feast. While Seithennin and his guests drank wine from the golden cups, Teithrin refrained from drinking, but kept a careful watch on everything.

78

When the feast was over Teithrin hastened to the palace of Gwyddno. It was a beautiful palace, built of white stone. It stood on the rocky banks of the river Mawddach, above the place where it ran into the plain of Cantre'r Gwaelod.

A guard stood at the castle gateway.

"Gwyddno holds a feast in the palace," said the guard. "None may enter the banqueting hall unless he be a prince."

"I am a prince. My name is Teithrin."

But the guard did not believe him.

"You must bring a witness to declare that you are a prince," he said.

Teithrin sat down on a great stone near the moat:

"I will go and seek Elphin, the son of King Gwyddno. He will declare unto the guard that I am Teithrin, the Prince."

The young Prince Elphin was fishing in the river Mawddach, in the higher reaches among the hills. He sat in the shadow of an ash-tree, watching the river swirl and eddy beneath. All was quiet save for the sound of the water. There was a sudden loud noise like the clash of thunder. Above it came the cry:

"Beware! Beware the oppression of Gwenhudiw."

Elphin sat up in terror. He knew that Gwenhudiw was a mermaid, the Shepherdess of the Deep. He knew that the white waves were her flock. Young Elphin paced the bank in terror. He knew that his father, Gwyddno, had also received the warning, "Beware the oppression of Gwenhudiw."

It was after receiving the warning that Gwyddno had come to live in this palace, staying as far away from the sea as he could. Elphin remembered how anxious his father had been after receiving the warning. He shuddered and looked round him. It was then that he saw a knight approaching him. Teithrin greeted him. Elphin answered, saying :

" I see you have travelled far. Who are you ? "

" I am Prince Teithrin. My father was Prince Tathal."

Elphin nodded : " I have heard your name. What brings you hither ? "

Teithrin answered : " I have come to seek the Prince of Cantre'r Gwaelod. I seek Elphin, the son of King Gwyddno."

" Did you call out as you came towards me ? " asked Elphin nervously.

" No," said Teithrin very surely. " No, I did not utter a word."

" But you did ! " cried Elphin. " You cried out, ' Beware the oppression of Gwenhudiw ! ' "

Teithrin denied that he had called out. He repeated that he had not uttered a word.

" Please do not argue about it," cried Teithrin ; " I have far more important news to relate."

He told Elphin how Prince Seithennin had neglected to repair the dyke, and how the land was in danger of being flooded by the sea.

" We will go together immediately to my father's palace," Elphin declared.

They hurried towards Gwyddno's palace.

" See here the fertile plain," cried Teithrin, " with its rich farms trusting in the defence of the dyke. See yonder in the sunset the great and hungry sea eager to flow over the land."

Elphin looked. " The dyke is our only defence," he said.

Again Teithrin tried to pass the guard at the gateway of Gwyddno's palace, but he was still not satisfied.

" I trust young Prince Elphin's word," he said, " but the prince is young. The stranger must bring another witness."

Impatient at this further delay Teithrin said : " I will go at once to the castle of the drunken Prince Seithennin. I will tell him of the warning you have heard."

" I will come with you," said young Elphin, eager to be of help.

They reached Prince Seithennin's palace, to find the prince and his courtiers feasting.

" Welcome, my merry men all," cried Prince Seithennin.

" We are but two," said Elphin. " On behalf of both, I, Prince Elphin, son of King Gwyddno, thank you."

The drunken Seithennin grew sober when he heard that the king's son was his guest.

" Be seated in the place of honour, my Prince," he cried, but Prince Teithrin spoke saying :

" You may honour the young prince in a feast on another day. We have come to see you on an urgent matter. That part of the dyke which is in your care has been neglected. It is no longer strong enough to withhold the sea."

Prince Seithennin struck the table with his clenched fist : " Yes, the dyke is old and broken in many places. But there is no danger, I assure you. I tell you truly there is no danger. Where is my page? Madoc, fill my silver cup with the flowing mead."

Prince Teithrin leaned across the table. "Listen, Seithennin," he said earnestly. "The stones of the dyke are loosened, the pillars are worn away, and each day the tide eats away the foundations."

"Aha! how wise you are," mocked Seithennin. "You, who would repair the excellent dyke built by the great builders of old. Fill yet another cup for me, Madoc."

The other guests lay around in drunken sleep.

"Come, Elphin," said Teithrin. "It were well that we leave this place. Seithennin will not see reason."

When they were about to leave the palace they saw a beautiful maiden.

"I am Rhonwen, the daughter of Prince Seithennin," she explained. "Let me take you to another part of my father's castle."

As the princes followed her across the entrance hall a mighty wind beat upon the castle walls from all directions. There was the sound of thunder, and after that a silence, and then a voice called out clearly:

"Beware the oppression of Gwenhudiw."

Teithrin ran to the dyke. He saw that a storm was approaching from every side.

"We are in great peril," he cried to Elphin and Rhonwen, who had followed him. "There will be floods in the rivers and streams, and the tide is high. The dyke will not hold."

"I have heard that voice before," said Rhonwen, searching the skies. " At my father's castle the winds blow from every side, and now it is the time of the full spring tide."

The wind sighed and soughed round them. Rhonwen clasped her cloak more closely about her. Followed by the two princes she ran back to the castle. The great noise had roused the drunken prince and his guests, and Prince Seithennin leaned against one of the pillars of the doorway. His sight was blurred, but he could see the water encroaching on the land. The spume of the waves blew inland, so that Prince Seithennin thought it was a snowstorm. Then the sound of the thunder confused him.

" Wake, father, wake ! " cried Rhonwen.

" The drunken guests still sleep," said Elphin.

" Hasten," cried Teithrin, " we must reach the east end of the castle."

The castle walls fell even as he finished speaking.

" Who is the enemy that attacks me ? " cried Prince Seithennin. " My guards ! Arm yourselves ! See, I have unsheathed my sword."

" Your sword is useless against this enemy," said Elphin bitterly.

" Who dares say that ? " demanded Seithennin. " Behold ! I go to prove the strength of my strong arm and my sharp sword."

Prince Seithennin leaped from the ruins of the castle wall and waded far into the angry tide.

" Father ! father ! " cried Rhonwen, holding out her arms, but Prince Seithennin was lost to sight under the sea.

Elphin tried to comfort her.

Prince Seithennin leaped from the ruins of the
castle wall

"We must leave this castle immediately," Prince Teithrin called, " or else we shall be buried in its ruins. Come, follow me."

Teithrin led the way. "Arm yourselves with spears," he called back. "Follow me to the top of the rampart."

Teithrin headed the procession. Rhonwen and Elphin followed. After them came some of the retainers and maids of the castle. Last of all came the bard. The storm continued. Slowly they made their way in the dim light of the moon. They thrust their spears into the rocky earth, and with their help withstood the attack of the wind. They clung to one another, praying that they would reach safety.

Towards dawn the tide turned, and in the light of day they saw the destruction the tide had caused. Teithrin stopped.

"Look around," he exclaimed. "The sea now covers the fertile plain of Cantre'r Gwaelod."

The pilgrims made their way to the palace of King Gwyddno.

"Welcome all!" cried the anxious king. "It is well that you have reached us in safety. There are others here from the homesteads near the shore. They heard the cry, 'Beware the oppression of Gwenhudiw.' They saw a great blazing light in the sky, and fled here for help."

They all gathered on the hills of Ardudwy. King Gwyddno spoke sadly: "The fertile land of Cantre'r Gwaelod now lies under the sea. Aberdovey was far inland. Now, see where it stands, close to the sea."

Years passed by. The land was never recovered. The plain of Cantre'r Gwaelod still lies under the sea.

If anyone doubts this story let him walk on the shore of Aberdovey at midnight. Sometimes far and sometimes near, faint and far away, he will hear sweet music as though of church bells ringing a tune known to all as " The Bells of Aberdovey."

## Y GWCW FACH

Gwcw fach, ond wyt ti'n ffoliog ?
Ffal di ral di rw, dw ri rai tai to.
Yn canu'n mhlith yr eithin pigog
Ffal di ral di rw ri, dw ri rai tai to.
  Dos i blwy' Aberdovey dirion
Ffal di ral di rw, di rai tai io ;
  Ti gei yno greigiau gwyrddion
Ffal di ral di rw, dw ri rai tai io.

## 20  OWEN'S STONE

NEAR the village of Gorslas in the county of Carmarthen, there lies a small lake known as Llyn Llech Owain, or the Lake of Owen's Stone. In the summer the waters are covered with the big leaves and white flowers of the water-lilies growing so abundantly there.

Many years ago people believed that a magic well lay near what is now the centre of Owen's Lake. The fairies looked after the well, and saw that the water was always pure and cool for the shepherds when they drove their flocks there to drink. A huge stone covered the mouth of the well. It was a rule that all who removed the stone and drank of the water should replace it after use.

One hot summer's day Sir Owen, a Knight of King Arthur's court, passed that way. He was returning to the home of his boyhood after weeks of fighting in a fierce war. The knight and his faithful steed were weary and very thirsty after their journey. There was no house in sight, and no tree offered friendly shade from the merciless rays of the sun.

Suddenly Sir Owen remembered the well. He encouraged his horse.

" On but a little way, Starlight. The well is at hand. We will drink deep of its cool waters."

They made their way to the magic well, and quenched their thirst in the pure water. Refreshed, Sir Owen lay down and fell asleep. The horse wandered away a little, nibbling at tufts of grass growing amidst the heather.

Half dreaming half waking, Sir Owen heard the waters of a rushing stream.

" What can it be ? " he exclaimed. " The rushing noise seems to surround me."

He sat up, then stood up in alarm. On every side lay a great stretch of water.

" It is my fault ! Alas ! it is my fault ! " cried Sir Owen, as he raised his hands in despair. " I forgot to replace the stone that covers the mouth of the well."

He looked round and saw that his horse was standing on a small slope of land. Sir Owen, grieving bitterly at what he had done, plunged into the water and swam to safety. The people

He sat up in alarm

of the village came and comforted the brave knight, for they knew of his many good deeds.

"See," they cried, pointing to the expanse of water, "is not this better? Now we have a lake where before we had but a small well."

In memory of the good knight they called the lake the Lake of Owen's Stone.

## 21 THE BRIDGE OF THE WHITE SPIRIT

IN Kidwelly Castle lived Sir Elidir Dhu, Knight of the Holy Sepulchre. He had two sons, Gruffydd and Rhys, and one daughter, Nest.

Sir Elidir called his young daughter to him.

"How like thy dead mother thou art!" he said.
"She too was fair and beautiful, gentle and kind."

Gladys, Nest's cousin, stood by, a dark scowl
on her face. How she hated the beautiful Princess
Nest.

Gladys paced the terrace of Kidwelly Castle.
Had her father, Philip, not been killed in battle
she would not have been obliged to seek shelter
in the home of her uncle, Sir Elidir. Gladys knew
that Gruffydd, her cousin, loved her, but she tossed
her dark head haughtily. She would marry a
greater prince than Gruffydd. Was she not de-
scended on her mother's side from the great Welsh
prince, Cadifor?

"Gladys, Gladys!" Nest called. "Wynne, the
blind harpist, is here. Come, cousin, he will play
and we will dance."

Gladys turned away, her mind filled with dark
thoughts of hatred against the lovely Princess Nest.

A little later Gladys discovered that Nest loved
a certain Norman knight who lived in the neighbourhood. He was called Sir Walter Mansell.

"Here is my chance," Gladys whispered to herself as she sat alone in her room in the south
tower. "I know my uncle does not approve of
this Norman knight. Shame on a Welsh princess
that she should love a Norman!"

Gladys sat brooding, thinking out plan after
plan. She paced her room, and then stood at her
window, watching the waters of the river Gwendraeth flow out to sea.

"I vow that I will destroy their love," she said.
"Gruffydd loves me, I know. I care naught for

him, but I will pretend I love him and so tell him evil things of Nest."

At this time a call to arms rang across Europe. The Holy Sepulchre—that is, the Tomb of Christ —was in danger of falling into the hands of the Saracen Turks. The clash of armour was heard in the courtyard of Kidwelly Castle as knights and pages prepared to answer the call. Sir Elidir left his home to join the crusade, and travelled far to join forces with those who went to fight for the Cross. With him went his younger son, Rhys. Gruffydd remained in charge of Kidwelly Castle during his father's absence.

Sir Walter Mansell's land lay in Glamorganshire, but he had an estate at Trimsaran, near Kidwelly. The knight often met Nest secretly at a bridge across the river Gwendraeth at a point midway between Kidwelly Castle and Sir Walter's home.

Gladys knew of these meetings, and carried evil tales to Gruffydd.

Among the servants and retainers at Kidwelly Castle was a man named Meurig Maney. He was crafty and cruel, but he held a place of importance in the castle, for he was a foster-brother of the Lady Gladys. Although of evil mind Meurig loved Gladys, and he was prepared to do anything that she bade him.

Gladys summoned Meurig to her room.

"Meurig, I trust you," she said. "You are my only faithful friend. If the Lord Gruffydd orders you to do something this evening you must do it, for the command is mine."

It was a fine evening in early autumn. Nest

hurried from the castle to her usual trysting-place.

"Here I come," she called gaily to her lover as she ran along a leaf-strewn path. "No-one could have a lover more faithful than thou, my Walter."

Sir Walter raised his hand in greeting. Nest saw him advancing to meet her. As he reached the middle of the bridge Sir Walter fell. At the same time a man who had been hiding in the trees near by sprang out upon the knight. Nest ran forward. She saw the assassin hurl her lover's body into the quick-flowing river below. Shrieking in horror, she jumped into the water after Sir Walter. Their bodies were carried out to sea, and a few days later were found on the quick-sands of Cefn Sidan, clasped in each other's arms.

The Lady Gladys was sitting in her bower when the fatal news was brought.

"A sad tale," she exclaimed to the maidens around her, "but there could be no happy ending when Nest loved Sir Walter. I had done all I could to save her from her foolishness." Gladys shrugged her shoulders. "Nest has brought this fate upon herself. I can only guess at what happened. The lovers must have tried to elope. The tide must have overtaken them, and so they were drowned."

Doubting the truth of Gladys' word the maidens moved away. On the parapets and in the court-yards they whispered to the grooms and pages. The men repeated the tale told by the fisherman who had found the bodies. They spoke of an ugly knife-wound near Sir Walter's heart, such a wound as only an assassin could have made.

Time passed on. When Sir Elidir, in the Holy Land, heard of the death of Nest, he died, broken-hearted.

Another crusade was proclaimed. More knights were needed to fight in the Holy Land, and Sir Gruffydd left Kidwelly Castle to join in the war. Among his followers was Meurig Maney. Soon after reaching Palestine Sir Gruffydd died. Sir Rhys was now the heir to Kidwelly Castle and all its lands. He returned home and married the Lady Gladys. She cared but little for her husband, nor in later years did she show any love for her sons, Nicholas and Thomas.

A heavy gloom hung over Kidwelly Castle. Few were happy there.

One day news was brought to the Lady Gladys that Meurig Maney had returned from the Holy Land to the castle.

" I must welcome him, I suppose," muttered Gladys sullenly, " for he is my foster-brother."

The messenger explained that Meurig was lying sick in his room. He was very weak, and the herb doctor had said he would not live.

Lady Gladys climbed the stone staircase to Meurig's room high in a lonely turret. The room was filled with the light of the setting sun, and in a shadowed corner a priest knelt holding a cross and praying.

" Come hither," Meurig beckoned to the lady and the priest. " I must tell my tale before I die. The spirit of Princess Nest has followed me since the day I killed Sir Walter. O how I have regretted my evil deed ! "

Lady Gladys tried to soothe the dying Meurig. She did not want the priest to know it was she who was to blame for the double tragedy. Meurig went on :

"Sleeping or waking, I hear the wild shriek of the beautiful Princess Nest. I had hoped that

" I must tell my tale before I die "

by joining in the crusade I would meet my death. I was punished severely in that I was spared to live."

Meurig paused for breath, for he was very weak. The priest broke the silence and prayed in Latin. The sick man raised himself on his straw pallet, his face wearing a strange expression, and his eyes looking wild and fierce.

" I have seen Nest again and again," he said.
" It was when Sir Elidir died that she first came
to me. She spoke so gently that I was yet more
ashamed at the evil I had done. She told me
her spirit was doomed to walk the earth because
she had taken her own life. Only when in years
to come a marriage shall take place between one
of her family and a member of the family of
Mansell will her spirit be at rest. Comforting me
then, she told me she would give warning of the
approaching death of each member of her family by
appearing on the Gwendraeth bridge."

Meurig sank back on his bed and died. The
Lady Gladys brooded long over the words he
had spoken.

Many declared that Meurig had spoken the truth
and that Nest often appeared at Pont Ysgrêch, or
the Bridge of the White Spirit.

Ffarwel i Blwy' Llangower
    A'r Bala dirion deg ;
Ffarwel fy anwyl gariad
    Nid wyf yn enwi neb.
'Rwyn mynd i wlad y Saeson
    A'm calon fel y plwm ;
I ddawnsio o flaen y delyn
    Ac i chwareu o flaen y drwm.

## 22  HYWEL AND THE MERMAID

On the rocks beyond Gwbert sat Hywel the
fisherman. He whistled a tune as he watched the
seagulls wheel and dip on the cliffs around him.

Suddenly he sat up. A little distance from where he was sitting, sat a mermaid. Never had Hywel seen anyone so beautiful.

He had stopped whistling in his surprise at seeing her. Quietly, on all fours, he crept nearer to see her more plainly. The mermaid was not aware that Hywel was staring at her. She sat singing in a voice as sweet and low as the little waves lapping in the shadowed pools in the sand. She combed her long loose tresses, pausing to gather the shells that hid and glistened in her golden hair.

" How beautiful she is ! " Hywel kept repeating. " I must take her home."

He tiptoed along the path until he was close beside her. Without saying a word he gathered her in his arms and bore her away into his boat.

The mermaid cried bitterly.

" Let me go—please, please let me go ! " she sobbed, but Hywel only shook his head.

" Tell me your name," he said.

" Modlen," said the mermaid. " Now, please, please let me go."

Hywel had made up his mind to keep her. He took her home and locked her in a room. Modlen, refusing to eat any of the food he brought her, continued to sob bitterly day and night.

" Let her go back with the next tide," said Maredudd, Hywel's friend, when told of the mermaid's cries.

" Maredudd is jealous," thought Hywel. " He is jealous because he did not catch the mermaid himself."

" She will cast a spell over you if you do not

let her go," Maredudd warned, but Hywel laughed, and said :

" I will do as I like and I mean to keep her."

As the months went by the mermaid grew thin and wan. " O Hywel, let me go back to my home," she pleaded. " If you will do that I will help you all I can. Should you be in danger on the sea I will come to you. I will warn you by calling to you three times, and I will lead you to safety."

Hywel thought a while, and then said to himself :

" Maredudd said she would curse me if I kept her. Now she promises to help me if ever I am in danger. I had better take her offer and let her go."

He gathered her in his arms, carried her to the shore, and kissing her said :

" Farewell, Modlen."

Many weeks passed by. Hywel had almost forgotten Modlen. One evening he was out fishing in his boat, when Modlen appeared at the prow.

" Hywel, Hywel, Hywel ! " she called. " Draw your net ! Hywel, Hywel, Hywel ! "

The sea was calm, and there were no signs of storm clouds in the sky.

" Modlen knows of some danger," Hywel said.

He rowed steadily back to harbour. The jeers and jests of the other fishermen echoed towards him over the quiet water. Scarcely had Hywel reached the haven when a great storm arose. Great clouds hung low over land and sea, and the waves rode high in the tempest.

The men of the fishing fleet were seen no more.

" I owe my life to Modlen," said Hywel, as he climbed to the weather-beaten church to give thanks for his safety.

## TRA BO DAU

Mae hon a gâr fy nghalon i
Yn mhell oddi yma yn byw,
A hiraeth am ei gweled hi
A'm gwnaeth yn llwyd fy lliw ;
Mil harddach yw y dêg ei llun
Na gwrid y wawr i mi
A thrysor mwy yw serch fy mûn
Na chyfoeth byd a'i fri.

*Chorus*
Cyfoeth nid yw ond oferedd
Glendid nid yw yn parhau ;
Ond cariad pur sydd fel y dur
Yn para tra bo dau.

## 23  THE DWARF'S REVENGE

On a farm called Ty-Gwyn in Monmouthshire there lived an old farmer. He had worked hard all his life, and now hoped to retire, having saved up much money.

"One thing I must do before we leave Ty-Gwyn," Lloyd the farmer said. "I will rid the farm of the fairies."

"You will never be able to do that," answered Cristin, his wife. "You have tried all your life. You will never succeed."

"I will go and consult the Witch of Skirrid," Lloyd answered. "She will help me."

The old witch cackled when Lloyd came to see her.

"You must pay me first," she said. "Bring me this day week three bucketfuls of the best cream. I will have the cream for my supper."

When Lloyd brought the cream the witch rubbed her gnarled hands as she explained to him how to rid his land of the fairies.

"Wherever you see the fairy circles on your land, sow there some corn."

Lloyd hastened home and carried out the advice of the Witch of Skirrid.

"Aha! They are gone!" cried Lloyd. "The fairies have all gone from the farm."

Lloyd and Cristin sat in the farmhouse kitchen.

"We will remain this year at Ty-Gwyn," they said, "and we will then move away to a new house."

In the spring, when his men were ploughing the fields, Lloyd met a little man in the lane. He was dressed in scarlet and carried a great sword.

"I am a herald," he cried in a high, thin voice. "I am sent to tell you that revenge will follow."

"Ha! ha!" laughed Lloyd. "Who will take revenge on me?"

"The fairies," answered the little man angrily.

In the summer the corn grew tall and strong. Lloyd walked about his fields and thought of the rich harvest that was to be his. There was a sudden noise.

" An earthquake ! " cried Lloyd, and shuddered.
But the sun shone and there was peace once more.

" All is well," said Lloyd to Cristin.

Harvest time came.

" It is time to gather the corn," said Lloyd.
" To-morrow we will begin to reap."

That night Lloyd and Cristin were wakened
from their sleep.

" The corn, Lloyd ! " exclaimed Cristin. " Ring
the great bell ! Cry for help ! The corn is on
fire ! "

On the farm-garth Lloyd met the little man in
scarlet. In one hand he carried his great sword,
in the other he bore a flaming torch.

" It is the fairies ! "
cried Lloyd. " The
fairies have burnt the
corn."

" Revenge ! " cried the
little man. " I told you
that revenge would come.
You have consulted the
witch, but beware, further
revenge is to follow."

Lloyd grew pale. He
shuddered, and begged
for mercy.

" I can give no mercy,"
answered the little man.
" I carry out the king's
command."

Lloyd asked him to beg the fairy king to be
merciful.

"Meet me here seven days hence," said the dwarf.

99

When the time came the dwarf said: "The King has seen that you are sorry. The curse will therefore not fall upon you but upon your descendants."

Lloyd and Cristin comforted each other. "It is well," they said. "The curse will pass. The fairies will forget."

When the old couple passed away their descendants lived at Ty-Gwyn.

"Revenge! Revenge!" The farmers of Ty-Gwyn heard the words whispered as they sowed corn and as they reaped it.

"What can it mean?" they asked one another.

Lloyd and Cristin had told no-one about the little dwarf and the revenge that would fall upon their descendants.

A hundred years had passed since Lloyd had heard the dwarf's message. Sieffre, the son of Rhisiart, lived with his father at Ty-Gwyn. Sieffre was to marry Eluned, the heiress of Ystrad.

As he walked home with her on Christmas Eve, there was a sound as of thunder and the earth shook. From the stream came a voice: "The time of revenge has come."

"What can that mean?" cried Eluned in terror.

Sieffre comforted her.

"We have imagined the words," he said. "We will forget them. Let us hasten to Ty-Gwyn. My mother has summoned many guests. They await our coming."

When they were seated at table at Ty-Gwyn there was a sudden thunder-clap. All were silent.

An old witch entered the room. Sieffre and Eluned clasped each other in fear.

Rhisiart was the first to recover from his fright.

"What do you want, old hag?" he demanded.

"Silence," snapped the witch. "I have come to tell you that the time of revenge upon this house has come." She disappeared.

The host and hostess did their best to comfort their guests, but the feast was ruined. All hurried homeward to tell of the strange sight they had seen and the stranger words they had heard.

"I will take Eluned home to Ystrad," said Sieffre.

He bade good-bye to Eluned at the entrance of her home. His parents awaited his coming that night, but Sieffre never returned. For days and weeks men and women searched for him on the hills and moorlands. They sought to comfort his parents, but they could find no trace of Sieffre's wanderings.

"We will go and consult the Hermit of the Fenni," said Rhisiart and his wife.

The Hermit shook his head sorrowfully when he heard their tale.

"The fairies have taken Sieffre," he said. "He may return, it is true, but, I fear, not in your lifetime."

The farmer and his wife returned to Ty-Gwyn. "We shall never see Sieffre again," they mourned.

But Eluned kept faith. "He will come, I feel sure," she said. "He will return as mysteriously as he disappeared."

All who heard smiled. Eluned felt quite sure that her lover would return. At sunrise and at sunset each day, she climbed to a hill behind the Ystrad and shading her eyes, she searched the moorland for some sign of Sieffre.

" I do not see him," she said, when she had grown very old. " I do not see him, but I still believe that he will come."

Years later Eluned died, still believing that Sieffre would return.

When Sieffre had said good-bye to Eluned on the Eve of Christmas so long ago, he had turned homeward. Hearing sweet voices carolling, he had followed in the direction of the music and met some goblin fiddlers who had led him into a great cave. There he had watched the fairies dance.

" I will go home now," at length said Sieffre, after what had seemed a few hours, and made his way to the mouth of the cave. He looked across the moor. The sun was high overhead.

" It is late," muttered Sieffre, " I have been out all night. I must hasten home to Ty-Gwyn."

He entered the house. An old man was seated on a settle in the kitchen.

" What brings you here ? " asked the old man, astonished that Sieffre should enter his house uninvited.

Sieffre was bewildered. " I am Sieffre," was all that he could say.

" You must be a stranger in these parts," the old man said. " I know of no-one by that name. But wait—yes, I have heard the name before. A man called Sieffre disappeared from this house of Ty-Gwyn more than a hundred years ago. I heard my grandfather speak of him when I was a child.''

" I am he." Sieffre began to sob.

" Comfort yourself." said the old man. " You shall be welcome at Ty-Gwyn. I will summon my grand-daughter. She will bring you food. Pray be seated here.''

He helped Sieffre to the ingle-nook, but at the touch of his hand Sieffre sank upon the hearth, and a small heap of dust was all that remained of him.

## 24  THE WELL OF SAINT TEGLA

In a farmhouse near the foot of Arenig there lived a farmer called Sion, his wife Nelw, and their only child, Wyn. They were a happy family. One thing alone worried them. Wyn was a healthy boy, but at times a strange disease overcame him, making him unconscious and to all appearances dead.

" Wyn will grow out of this sickness," the neighbours said. " Mark our words, he will grow into a man, brave and strong."

But Sion and Nelw were not to be comforted. They watched carefully over their son. When he was well they rejoiced together, but when the strange disease came they would sit and shake their heads sorrowfully.

Wyn was now twelve years old. In the spring-time he was so well that it seemed as if the disease had left him. Sion and Nelw watched him but their hearts were sorrowful.

"The apple-tree is bearing its blossoms far too early this year." Nelw shook her head sorrowfully. "It is an evil omen."

Sion answered, "A far worse omen is the crowing of the cockerel at night. If it crows through this night until daybreak I will cut off its head."

The next morning Sion came in from the poultry-yard.

"Grieve no more, Nelw. No more will that cockerel foretell the death of our young son. I have killed it."

"Alack!" answered Nelw. "Of what use is it? Throughout the night I kept dreaming. I dreamt that I was at a wedding. Dreams go by opposites. Soon I shall be at our son's funeral."

Scarcely had she finished speaking when they heard a strange scraping sound at the kitchen window. They turned and saw a bird flapping its wings against the panes.

"It is the Bird of Death!" cried Nelw, raising her hands in horror.

Sion tried to comfort her, himself sad at heart. How very dearly they loved their son, and he was to be taken from them!

A few days later Sion was walking home from Bala, laden with stores for the house. He was walking along a lonely stretch of road. From a cluster of trees near the roadside there came an old witch. Sion shook with fear. He saw her long cloak drag in the mud of the roadway, and for long he was so afraid that he did not dare raise his eyes to her face.

When he did so it was to see the wrinkled features of an old hag. Her black eyes shone in their hollow sockets; her nose was long and beaked, and her black teeth jutted out from thick purple lips. A horrible sight, thought Sion, and hid deeper in the shadows where he stood.

Sion thought she was going to come and speak to him, but she walked past him as though she had not seen him. She slid down into a little ditch

He saw a candle travelling in front of him

at the side of the road, and there she bathed her feet. She screamed several times, raising the echoes in the great wood beyond.

"My child! My child!" she screeched. "My dear, dear son."

The words were carried to Sion by the gentle south-west wind. He repeated them to himself and shuddered.

" The witch is claiming Wyn," he said. " I must hasten home and warn Nelw."

He hurried on, but he had only gone a little way when he saw a candle travelling in front of him.

" A corpse-candle," cried Sion, for it was a sight which men believed foretold a death. " It is a red candle," said Sion in a whisper. " That is a sign that it is the body of a boy ! " He walked on a few paces : " It is a small candle. That shows that it is the body of a child."

Great was Sion's astonishment to find, when he reached home, that Wyn was alive. The boy was sleeping peacefully, unaware of the strange signs seeming to foretell his death. Sion told his tale to Nelw. She clutched his arm.

" To-morrow, Sion," she said, " you shall harness the horse and ride to Trawsfynydd. You will ask the wizard there what we can do to keep our son." She opened a small coffer and counted out some gold : " Tell him we will pay him well if only he tells us what we can do to keep Wyn."

When Sion returned, Nelw ran to the kitchen to hear him repeat the wizard's advice. This he did point by point.

" We will do all that the Wise Man says," she cried. " This very moment I will begin to prepare for you to take the boy to the Well of Saint Tegla in the county of Denbigh."

Well stocked with provisions they set out for Llandegla. Sion rode the mare, Wyn the pony.

" Blessings on your journey," said Nelw from her heart as she waved good-bye.

When they reached Llandegla Sion arranged that Wyn should carry out the wizard's instructions. At sunset Wyn went to the Well of Saint Tegla, carrying a basket containing a cockerel. He drank of the water and then threw some drops over his left shoulder.

"Now walk round the well three times," commanded Sion, "and as you do so repeat the Lord's Prayer."

When Wyn had done so Sion said, "You will do the same again, but this time you will walk the pony around the church."

"I grow tired, father," said Wyn when he had done so.

"You may rest now," said Sion, and he led his son into the church.

Sion placed the Bible as a pillow beneath the altar. "Rest there till morning, my son," he said, and he placed the altar cloth over the lad as a covering.

In the morning Sion came to fetch Wyn.

"We will place a golden coin on the altar as an offering," he said, "and we will leave the fowl here as the wise man has ordered."

Sion and Wyn set out for home. The lad whistled merrily. Sion was troubled in mind concerning the fate of the cockerel he had left in the church.

"If it does not die," he muttered, "then Wyn will die. But if it does die then Wyn will be safe."

Nelw welcomed the travellers back to the farm.

"I have been praying all day," she said, "that the strange disease that attacks Wyn shall now leave him. May it attack the fowl in church instead!"

The next three weeks were an anxious time for Sion and Nelw. News travelled slowly in those days, but at length there came a messenger to say that the cockerel was dead. Sion and Nelw rejoiced.

"This means," they exclaimed, "that the strange disease that has defied the doctors and so often attacked our son is now gone from the earth."

They called Wyn, who rejoiced with them. Nelw set about preparing a feast and called on her neighbours to join in the celebration.

Wyn grew well and strong. Despite the evil omens he did not die that spring; and perhaps because his parents had carried out the words of the Wise Man of Trawsfynydd he grew up to be brave and strong and lived to a ripe old age.

## Y PREN AR Y BRYN

Ar y bryn 'roedd pren,
  O bren braf!
Y pren ar y bryn a'r bryn ar y ddaear
  A'r ddaear ar ddim.
Ffeind a braf oedd y bryn
  Lle tyfodd y pren.

Ar y pren daeth cainc,
  O gainc braf!
Y gainc ar y pren, y pren ar y bryn
  Y bryn ar y ddaear a'r ddaear ar ddim—
    Ffeind a braf oedd y bryn
    Lle tyfodd y pren.

## 25  OWEN OF THE RED HAND

HERE is the story of how a drover chanced to behold a Welsh chieftain who had lived in days so long ago that they are now lost in myth and mystery.

A young drover named Dafydd often drove cattle from Cardiganshire to London. One day when passing through Llandebie, a small village in Carmarthenshire, he cut himself a stout stick to help him in his task of driving the cattle.

A few days later Dafydd was sitting in an inn near London. He had delivered the cattle to their owner, and he was now preparing to return to his home. He felt very lonely as he sat in the inn. He clutched his stick with both hands. A man, dressed strangely and wearing a great black cloak came up to Dafydd and asked:

"Ah, my lad, from what country do you come?"

"I come from Wales, sir," answered Dafydd.

The stranger's eyes shone. Dafydd withdrew a little. There was something weird and magical about this man. The stranger took Dafydd's stick. He examined it closely and said:

"You cut this stick from a hedge of hazel branches in a small lane near Llandebie."

Dafydd looked up in surprise. His amazement grew as the stranger described in detail the exact place where the stick had been growing.

"You are surprised at my words, young lad,"

said the stranger, " but you would be yet more surprised were you to see the wonderful things to be found under the place where that stick was growing."

Dafydd was silent. He had grown tongue-tied at the stranger's words.

" I am a wanderer myself," the man continued. " It matters but little to me where I travel. To-morrow, I understand, you mean to return to Wales. I will go with you."

They made the journey on foot. Dafydd was **very** impatient for he was anxious to see the **strange** things his companion had described. When they reached the road that lies between Llandebie and Golden Grove the two men made their way to a tree at the foot of Dinas.

" This is the tree where you cut the magic stick," said the man.

Dafydd nodded.

" Run to that farmhouse," said the man, " and borrow two spades. Tell them also that we will need a night's lodging."

Dafydd did as he was told. When he returned, the two began to dig at the foot of the tree from which the stick had been cut.

It was noon when they started their task. The sun had set and night was falling when suddenly they fell through some loose earth into a great room. When their eyes had grown accustomed to the dim light there, they saw that the room was a great hall. The ceiling was supported by old oaken beams, black with age. The walls were adorned with weapons and ornaments of a time long past.

The stranger stood in the shadows, but he urged Dafydd to enter the room. Dafydd now realized that there was someone else in the great hall. He made his way along, and saw that at the far end of a long table a man was sitting.

Dafydd looked at him closely. He saw that he was very handsome and that he had the body of a strong man and a trained warrior. Seated in a great chair the man was sleeping quietly. His head rested on his left hand. His right hand, red and bloodstained, hung at his side, grasping a great sword. At his feet slept a great mastiff.

On tiptoe Dafydd crept closer.

He examined the beautiful carved table that stood before the great warrior. Stacked in neat piles upon it were coins of gold, stamped with the faces of ancient British kings. Dafydd started suddenly as a voice broke the silence. He turned to find that the stranger was beckoning him to return to the entrance of the hall.

When Dafydd was alongside him, the strange man said in a hushed voice:

" Let me explain all this to you, Dafydd. You, my dear lad, have been chosen among all Welshmen of this generation to see the mighty Owen of the Red Hand."

Dafydd looked puzzled.

" There he is, Dafydd," said his companion, pointing with his hand to the sleeping warrior. " There is Owen Llawgoch, Owen of the Red Hand. He has been sleeping there for hundreds and hundreds of years. When the time is ripe, when the appointed signal is given him, Owen will wake and claim his throne—the throne of

Britain. That sword in his Red Hand is an heirloom of the ancient kings. Never yet has it been drawn except for victory."

Dafydd expressed amazement at all he had seen. "You may come here as often as you like, Dafydd, for you have been chosen to see these strange sights," the man explained. He laid his hand on Dafydd's shoulder, and speaking very solemnly said, "I must warn you of one thing. You must take *nothing* away from this hall."

Accepting his friend's advice, Dafydd agreed not to remove anything, and together they left the strange room. They then made their way to the farmhouse where they had arranged to spend the night.

Next morning Dafydd rose up early, and running to the foot of the tree, he climbed down quickly into the hall. Things were just as they had been before. Owen of the Red Hand slept peacefully, and his dog slumbered at his feet.

Dafydd went round the room examining many things. When he reached Owen's chair he saw that a gold coin had fallen to the floor.

"I did not notice that coin there yesterday," said Dafydd to himself. Moved by curiosity he stooped down and picked up the coin. He examined the gold piece curiously.

"I have never seen anything like this before," he said. "There can be no harm in taking this with me. There are many hundreds of coins left on the table."

He was, however, uneasy in his mind about taking the gold coin, yet he continued to persuade himself. "If I take it and show it to people, then they will believe me when I tell them of this weird old hall."

He put the coin in his pocket. Feeling more than a little frightened, he looked back over his shoulder. Owen was still sleeping. He had not

He stooped down and picked up the coin

seen Dafydd take the coin. Dafydd sighed with relief. Yet he remained cautious and tiptoed out of the hall.

When he reached the surface he examined the coin in the light of day. How it glittered in the sunlight! Would it not be well to collect a sack-load of gold coins ? They were useless there in the gloomy cavern.

Dafydd ran to an outhouse of the farm to fetch a sack. He returned to gather up the booty. But where—O where was the entrance ? Dafydd searched long and diligently, but never again did he find the way in, or a trace of the strange man who had accompanied him.


## 26  THE PHYSICIANS OF MYDDFAI

In the north of Carmarthenshire is a small village, nestling in the hills, called Myddfai. Not far from Myddfai is Llyn Y Van, or Van Pool. The pool is a small lake set in a countryside that is wild and desolate. One can wander for many miles without meeting a single creature.

Long ago there lived near this lake a peasant woman and her son, Rhiwallon. Rhiwallon's father had been killed fighting the Normans when they came to conquer Wales. The widow and her son worked very hard for their living on the small mountain farm.

Rhiwallon's duty was to take care of the herds that grazed on the hillside. He liked his work, and often spent the lonely hours of his watch in carving beautiful things in wood.

One evening he was returning home, tired after his day's work. When he reached the bottom of the great crag towering over Van Pool he stood still in astonishment. A herd of ghost-like oxen was coming from the pool.

Rhiwallon watched the oxen climb on to some pastureland. He grew more astonished when he saw that the herd was being driven by a swan, which suddenly turned into a most beautiful maiden.

Rhiwallon had lived so much alone that he was very shy of speaking to anyone except his mother. When he saw the beautiful maiden, however, he forgot his shyness. He ran up to her, and when he held out his hands towards her she gave him a piece of bread.

"Take it," she said in a sweet voice. "Take it and eat it as a sign of friendship."

He did so. She laughed and vanished. Then Rhiwallon looked round for the strange oxen. They too were not to be seen. He rubbed his eyes. Had he been dreaming? Surely not! He was certain the beautiful maiden had spoken to him. Bowing his head, quite at a loss, he made his way home to tell his mother of the strange adventure.

Rhiwallon continued his work of taking care of the herds on the lonely hills. As the days went by his thoughts centred more and more on the beautiful maiden. He longed to see her again, but though he searched throughout each day he could not find her.

It was New Year's Eve. The lads of the village of Myddfai called to Rhiwallon.

"It is the night of Nos Calan! Come, Rhiwallon, we will have a gay time together in the village."

But Rhiwallon turned away. His mother ran after him and tried to persuade him to join the merry party. Rhiwallon explained to his mother that he wanted to be alone to think of the lovely maiden he had seen. The mother shook her head sadly, and Rhiwallon, turning up a path that led to the mountainside, made his way to the lonely lake.

A full moon sailed high in the sky. Rhiwallon saw that a heavy mist hung over the lake. As he gazed he saw something moving on the surface of the water close by. Very quietly the lad crept nearer, and saw that the object floating on the water was a piece of bread. He reached out and took it.

" She said that bread was a token of friendship," he muttered to himself. " I will eat this small crust."

Hardly had he done so when he heard a rustling in the waters of the lake. Rhiwallon looked and saw the strange herd of oxen approaching as before.

" This time," exclaimed Rhiwallon, " there is no swan following them, but there is something else." He peered into the shadows, and then the moon lit up the waters. " It is a little golden boat ! " he exclaimed.

When the boat reached the lakeside out stepped the beautiful lady whom Rhiwallon had seen before.

" This time she shall not escape me," declared Rhiwallon. He ran to her and told her that he loved her.

" I love you too, Rhiwallon," said the beautiful lady.

Rhiwallon led her to his home. On the way thither the Lady of the Lake told Rhiwallon that she was willing to marry him. Rhiwallon was overjoyed, but the lady raised her hand in warning.

"You are a mortal, Rhiwallon. I am immortal. There must therefore be one condition on which I marry you."

Rhiwallon declared he did not care what the

Out stepped the beautiful lady whom Rhiwallon had seen before

condition was if only the Lady of the Lake would stay with him. Looking very sad, she then said, "If ever you should strike me three times I must return alone to the place whence I came."

Rhiwallon laughed aloud. "I accept the condition," he said boldly. "It is not likely that I shall ever strike thee whom I love so much."

Rhiwallon's mother welcomed the Lady of the Lake. When she was told of the condition on which the young couple could be married, she, like Rhiwallon, laughed aloud. It was not likely that her son would strike the fair lady. Had he not sought long and patiently to possess her?

The young couple were married. They lived very happily.

"We shall grow rich," said the Lady of the Lake. "I possess great herds of oxen. They shall be yours and shall graze on the mountainside."

Wealth was theirs. They owned sheep and cattle and wide stretches of pasture land. Their greatest treasure, however, was their family of brave sons and beautiful daughters.

The old condition governing their married life was far from Rhiwallon's mind when one day he and his wife made their way to the church at Myddfai to attend a christening. The guests were bidding farewell at the church door. Rhiwallon was anxious to return to his farm. In order to summon his wife, he tapped her lightly on the shoulder with his glove.

"Beware, Rhiwallon, beware!" cried the Lady of the Lake.

Rhiwallon looked at her in astonishment.

"Remember the old warning," she said in great distress. "You have struck me once."

Many years went peacefully by. Rhiwallon had again forgotten the condition, when he and his wife went to a wedding. The guests at the wedding feast were merry, all save the Lady of the Lake. She burst into tears and cried bitterly, refusing to be consoled, for in a vision she could see the troubles and sorrows that lay ahead for the newly married couple.

Rhiwallon went to her and scolded her, telling her that she was damping the pleasure of the other guests.

"Come, come, dear wife," he said coaxingly. "I know you can be the happiest creature in the world."

He touched her lightly on the arm, bidding her join the merry folk.

"Rhiwallon!" she exclaimed through her tears. "O my dear husband! You have now struck me twice. Only once more remains."

Rhiwallon promised he would take great care in the future not to strike her. Many, many months passed and all was well.

Rhiwallon's friend who lived in a neighbouring farm died. Rhiwallon and his wife attended the funeral. All were sad in the house of mourning. Suddenly the silence was broken by peals of fairy laughter. The Lady of the Lake was laughing at the sorrowful faces around her, for she remembered that Rhiwallon's friend was now in a state of happiness with all his sorrows past. Rhiwallon knew that merry laugh. He ran to his wife and scolded her. In doing so he touched her lightly on the arm.

The Lady of the Lake grew thin and pale. She said, very faintly:

"Farewell, my dear, dear husband. You have struck me the third and last time."

Her form changed. Rhiwallon saw her as he had first seen her, and then she vanished from his sight. He ran to the mountainside and then to the lake, hoping to overtake her. He called and watched till sunset, but saw no trace of her.

Months and years passed by, but the Lady of the Lake did not return. Grief-stricken, Rhiwallon remained at the lakeside, seeking some news of her. Oftentimes his sons and his daughters waited with him, for they too were in great sorrow.

One night the sons were watching by the Van Pool. They saw something appear ; it was really their mother as their father had first seen her, but they did not recognize her, and turned away heartsore. The Lady of the Lake called :

" My sons ! My sons ! "

They knew her voice and ran to kiss her. She told them that they might only kiss her hands. Then as they knelt before her she blessed them.

" Your work, my sons," she said, " is to become great physicians. You must heal the suffering."

They looked at her in surprise. She knew that they were farmers, tending Rhiwallon's herds, but the mother went on :

" Have no fear, my noble sons. I will tell you of the healing herbs. I will guide your footsteps to the places where they grow."

Having said these words the Lady of the Lake grew thin and vanished.

The sons hurried home to tell their father of the strange meeting. Rhiwallon told them that they must obey their mother. He and his daughters would take care of the flocks and herds.

Rhiwallon's sons climbed the mountainsides. Guided by their mother's invisible form they collected goodly herbs to heal the sick. They became very skilful and reports of their healing powers spread all over Britain. The Lord Rhys, owner of the greater part of South Wales, gave them lands and bestowed great honours on them.

When Rhiwallon's sons died their sons in turn became skilled doctors. For many generations their skill was preserved in the family.

Some of the knowledge was written down in a book that we can still read, called *The Physicians of Myddfai*. Many of the cures seem very strange, though not so strange when we remember that they were suggested by the Lady of the Lake.

### CYFRI'R GEIFR

Oes gafr eto ?
Oes, heb ei godro
Ar y creigiau geirwon serth
Mae'r hen afr yn crwydro.
Gafr wen, wen, wen
Ie finwen, finwen, finwen
Foel gynffonwen
Foel gynffonwen
Ystlys wen a chynffon
    Wen, wen, wen.

## 27 PRESCRIPTIONS OF THE PHYSICIANS OF MYDDFAI

A COLD mouth and warm feet will live long.

Good are a salmon and a sermon in Lent.

Suppers kill more than the Physicians of Myddfai can cure.

A light dinner and less supper, sound sleep, and a long life.

If thou desirest to die, eat cabbage in August.

### To oblige a Man to confess what He has done wrong

Take a frog alive from the water. Extract its tongue and put him back again in the water. Lay this same tongue on the heart of the sleeping man, and he will confess his deeds in his sleep.

### A way in which things can be seen which are invisible to others

Take the gall of a cat and hen's fat, mixing them together. Put this in your eyes, and you will see things which are invisible to others.

### To extract a Tooth without Pain

Take some newts, by some called lizards, and those nasty beetles which are found in ferns during summer, calcine them in an iron pot, and make a powder thereof. Wet the forefinger of the right hand, insert it in the powder, and apply it to the tooth frequently, refraining from spitting it off, when the tooth will fall away without pain. It is proven.

## 28 TWM SHÔN CATTI, THE WELSH ROBIN HOOD

TWM SHÔN CATTI is the Welsh Robin Hood. He was a gay adventurer who robbed the rich to give to the poor. His home is said to have been in a cave which is still to be seen near the source of the river Towy in the county of Carmarthen. West and mid-Wales were the scenes of his wildest escapades.

There are many tales told about him, but we cannot say that they are true. This we do know. Twm was born about the year 1530, and he was the son of a certain Catti or Catherine. When he was a young man he lived a very wild life. But after he had married a rich lady he lived in a fine old house near Tregaron, and became a landowner of great importance.

These are the amusing stories of some of his adventures.

One day Twm met a wicked highwayman. Twm was a highwayman himself, and he wanted to outwit the other. It was a cold, wintry day. Twm rode a weary old horse, and his saddle-bags were filled with a load of sea-shells. He was dressed like a poor farmer ; no-one would have recognized him as Twm Shôn Catti the highwayman.

Twm rode past a knoll where he knew the highwayman lay in ambush. When he was abreast of him, the villain ran out.

" Your money or your life ! " he demanded.

Twm pretended to be terrified.

" Have mercy ! " he begged. But the highwayman only repeated his threat.

" Alas and alack," wailed Twm, " that this should befall me. But my life is of greater worth than this."

He loosened his saddle-bags and threw them over the hedge.

" Curse you ! " cried the highwayman, as he

scrambled through the thicket after them. " Curse you ! Can you not be more polite ? "

Twm watched him stoop for the saddle-bags on the other side of the hedge. In a trice Twm leapt from his weary old horse, and was soon astride the fine steed of the highwayman.

" Now, my beauty," he coaxed, stroking the horse's neck, " gallop your fastest."

A touch of the spurs and the horse was away like a flash of lightning.

The highwayman saw too late what had happened. He stamped and cursed, but far away in the next valley Twm was praising his new horse, and plundering the well-filled saddle-bags.

Twm went to a fair in Llandovery. He stood near a stall where a woman was selling Welsh flannel. Twm watched her as she gossiped busily with a customer.

Slyly he fastened the end of the roll of cloth to his coat and hurriedly made his way through the busy crowd.

Later in the day Twm passed the woman's stall again. She was gossiping more busily now, telling all who came that way how she had lost a roll of cloth.

Twm listened and pretended he was sorry.

" Oho ! " he said. " In future you must do as I do. Fasten your cloth to your coat. Then it cannot be stolen."

Another well-known story about Twm is the one that tells how he stole a bull and then sold it back to the owner. Having stolen the bull he took it to market to sell it, disguising the animal by fastening a long, bushy artificial tail to its real tail. So clever was Twm that he persuaded the real owner of the bull to buy it from him at a goodly price.

George Borrow, a traveller who loved the old stories of Wales, wrote a book called *Wild Wales*. He tells an amusing story of Twm's adventure in a shop in Llandovery.

" I need to buy a porridge pot," Twm declared in a loud voice when he entered the shop.

The ironmonger brought several pans and cauldrons so that Twm might choose among them.

" I see a hole in this one," said Twm, holding one up to the light.

The shopman examined it.

" I cannot see a hole," he said.

" Come to the doorway," said Twm. " Now, put your head closer and you will see it."

Twm stepped forward and brought the saucepan hard down on the ironmonger's head. Twm then gathered up the pots and pans and ran out past the blindfolded and bewildered shopman.

On the roadway Twm stopped to laugh, and cried, " Friend, had there been no hole there you would not have got your head inside."

Twm is said to have married the heiress of Ystrad Ffin. The facts of Twm's life do not bear out the tale, but the story is a pretty one.

Twm saved Rhinedd Price from the hands of a highwayman.

" How can I repay you for your kind deed ? "
cried the lady.

" By marrying me," said Twm with a smile.

" That I cannot do," said Rhinedd sorrowfully.

She asked Twm to her beautiful home, and
invited him to dine with her and her elderly

" Friend, had there been no hole there you would not
have got your head inside "

husband. Twm enjoyed himself, and in taking
his leave whispered to Rhinedd :

" I will marry you when your husband dies."

Rhinedd smiled and gave her consent. A few
years later Esquire Price died. Twm heard of this
and rode fast and furiously to the house at Ystrad
Ffin for the fulfilment of the promise.

At first Rhinedd refused to see Twm. She

remembered her promise, and loved Twm, but she did not wish to marry a highwayman. Twm sent the maid-servant into the house to beg for one last meeting.

" My mistress will come to her window to-morrow night," reported the maid-servant. " She will see you there."

At the appointed time Twm came to Rhinedd's window, and the lady stretched forth her hand in greeting. Twm held her hand fast and said :

" Rhinedd, my fairest ! I swear by all that is holy that I will cut off your hand with my sword unless you promise faithfully that you will marry me."

" You jest, Twm," cried Rhinedd.

" By faith, never was I more serious ! " exclaimed Twm. " As proof of my intention, feel you the edge of my sword."

When he drew the cold steel across Rhinedd's arm the lady yielded.

Twm and Rhinedd were married in the little church at Ystrad Ffin. Twm became a great land-owner and a Justice of the Peace. When he died he was a wealthy squire, much respected and much beloved.

## Y PEROT PURLON

Ai di'r Perot Purlon pêr
Tua godre'r Sir mae 'm siwrnai
At y ferch lle rhos i'm serch
I ddywedyd hyn o leiniau ?
Dos di whaff, na fydd yn hir
Ti gei'r dydd yn hir yn mhob man.
Cei'r gwynt o'r De a'r ffordd yn glir
O bydd gywir i mi, rwan !

## HWB I'R GALON

I ba beth y byddaf brudd
  Ie, pam y byddaf brudd
I ba beth y byddaf brudd
  A throi llawenydd heibio ?
    Tra 'rwyf yn ieuanc ac yn llon
      Ie'n ieuanc ac yn llon
    Tra 'rwyf yn ieuanc ac yn llon
      Rhof hwb i'r galon eto.
  Ton ton dyri ton ton ton
  Ton ton ton dyri ton ton ton
    Dyri ton ton ton.

## 29  MERLIN

THE wizard Merlin is the hero of many legends. He was sometimes called Merlin Sylvester or Merddin Wyallt, and is said to have lived in Caer-fyrddin, Carmarthen.

Tales of Merlin were written in very early times.

King Vortigern wished to build a city and fortress in the kingdom of Gwynedd, a district of mid-Wales. The king's wise men led him to a wild region near the summit of Snowdon.

"Command, O King," they cried, "that masons and carpenters set to work to collect the stone and wood, and order them to build."

The king did as they advised, but a strange thing happened. All the materials that the workmen had collected disappeared in the night. The wise men took counsel together. Their leader spoke to King Vortigern, advising him to break the evil spell:

"You must find a fatherless child. Put him to death, and sprinkle with his blood the ground on which the fortress is to be built. If you neglect to do this you will never build the fort."

King Vortigern paid heed to the words of the wise men. Messengers travelled far and wide to seek the fatherless child. At length they came to a field near Carmarthen, where a group of boys were playing at a game of ball.

"No good will come to you, you boy without a father," cried one of the boys to the lad who had possession of the ball.

The messengers beckoned to the boy. They questioned him and then carried him away to King Vortigern. When the king's men were ready to kill the boy Merlin laughed. He spoke in a clear voice, and told them that his death would not help them in their work. Then turning to King Vortigern he said:

"Command your workmen to dig into the ground, and you will find a pond which causes the foundation of your fortress to sink."

The workmen dug deep and came to the pond.

"Dig deeper yet," cried Merlin. "You will find something strange."

The workmen continued to dig until they came to two great hollow stones.

"A strange sight, in truth," exclaimed King Vortigern.

"Come nearer," said Merlin. "Examine them."

Inside the stones were two dragons asleep. When they awoke they fought.

"What means this?" asked the king in alarm.

Merlin turned aside to hide his tears.

"It means," he said, as he pointed to the two dragons fighting, "that two nations will fight. Behold the Yellow Dragon is the Saxon, the Red Dragon is the Celt."

"Which will win?" cried King Vortigern.

But Merlin only smiled the strange mysterious smile of a wizard, and the two dragons were lost to sight in a heavy mist.

## 30  ARTHUR BECOMES KING

KING UTHER PENDRAGON lay on his death-bed. He sighed and said:

"I grieve that I live to see this day. The Saxons harry the whole of Britain."

He sank back on his pillows, and there were some who thought that he was dead. Merlin, the wizard, sat at the bedside.

" King Uther is not dead," he said, " he sleeps. For three days he will remain sleeping thus."

On the third day King Uther awoke.

" It is good to be awake," he said feebly, " and to feel the glow of the sun again."

The courtiers crowded around to hear him, for his voice was weak and faint.

" Such a strange dream I have had," said King Uther. " It seemed to me that I saw two dragons fighting. One was red and the other was yellow, and I cannot say which was the more fierce. The red dragon was vanquished first, but it recovered strength, and growing more fierce in its anger drove the yellow dragon from the field of contest. Then a mist shrouded everything. When the mist had cleared I saw the red dragon striding over the field, proud of its victory. What can be the meaning of this strange dream, O wise Merlin ? "

Merlin rose to answer the king.

" You have seen a vision, mighty Uther," he explained. " The red dragon will be summoned from among your people to banish the pagans from our land."

" Your words comfort me," said King Uther. " Let it be known," he added, " that I wish to speak to the overlords of my realm."

The princes and dukes assembled.

" I am dying," said King Uther, " and in your presence I wish to name my successor. It is my desire that my son, Arthur, shall succeed to my throne. And now, may God receive my soul."

" We will honour King Uther's body," the overlords said. They buried him with great reverence where St. Paul's Cathedral now stands.

On Christmas Day the archbishop summoned the overlords together to the banks of a great lake. When they were all assembled there was a loud noise like the sound of thunder. It drew dark, and there were flashes of lightning. Then calm followed and the sun shone.

" Behold ! " cried the archbishop. He pointed over the waters of the lake. A huge stone stood in the midst, and wedged in it was a mighty sword with a jewelled hilt. On the blade was carved an inscription in Latin.

The archbishop translated it to the waiting princes. " He who can withdraw this sword from the stone, he is the true king of Britain."

The knights rowed out to the great stone, which was shaped like an anvil. Each rowed out with his heart full of hope, and tried to pull the beautiful sword from the stone. Each rowed back disappointed that he had failed to gain possession of the sword, Excalibur.

Arthur, whom King Uther had named king, was not at the lake side. He was riding towards London with Sir Hector and Sir Hector's son, Sir Kay. Merrily they rode towards the fair city until Sir Kay cried :

" Alas, I have ridden forth and my sword is not within its scabbard."

Sir Hector answered impatiently :

" It is too late to ride back to our castle. I need thee to attend to our business, and our retainers wait for us."

" *I* will fetch thy sword," cried Sir Arthur. " It will not be long before I have ridden back to join thee."

The young knight loved his foster-brother, Sir Kay, and was pleased to ride back upon the errand.

When Arthur reached Sir Hector's castle he could not enter. The drawbridge was raised, and though the young knight managed to cross the moat he could not gain entrance, for the great doors were locked and barricaded.

Disappointed, Arthur rode back to join Sir Hector and Sir Kay. As he was riding near the lake of St. Paul's he saw the stone and the sword thrust into it. An old man explained to him what the archbishop had said.

"He grows old, his mind is wandering," said Arthur, "but I will try to get that sword for my foster-brother."

There was no-one at the lakeside when Arthur rowed out to the great stone anvil.

"A beautiful sword, in truth," exclaimed Arthur. He grasped the sword by its jewelled hilt and drew it forth with ease.

"Excalibur," he said, reading the inscription on the sword. "I will hasten onward and give Excalibur to Kay."

"You have lingered on your journey," said Sir Kay in anger when Arthur arrived. "This is not my sword, but give it me at once."

Handing him the sword, Arthur told him the strange story attached to the beautiful weapon.

"The sword is mine!" Sir Kay's eyes shone with greed. "Remain there until I return."

Sir Kay sought his father.

"Behold, sire!" he cried. "This is the magic sword of the stone anvil in the lake. In truth I, Sir Kay, am the lawful king of Britain."

Sir Hector took the sword, examined it closely, then leapt on his fine steed and called to his son: " Ride with me."

Together they rode to the silent lake.

" It is Excalibur," cried Sir Hector, " but thou, my son, must swear upon the Holy Book that thou thyself didst draw it forth out of the stone anvil."

Sir Kay grew pale. He shuddered and fell upon his knees. " Mercy, sire! " he begged. " Mercy, and I will tell thee how it was I came into possession of the magic sword."

When Sir Kay had finished Sir Hector said, " It is Arthur who is King of Britain. King Uther's wish is granted. True are Merlin's words. When Arthur was placed in my care as an infant the great magician declared that he would live to rule this realm."

Then Arthur arrived at the lakeside.

" Take this sword, my son," said Sir Hector, " and place it back in the stone anvil."

Arthur rowed out and replaced the sword. " Now bring it hither," Sir Hector called.

When Arthur came back Sir Hector and Sir Kay removed their helmets, and kneeling in their armour called out:

" We hail thee, King Arthur."

" Arise! " cried Arthur. " Here come the Archbishop and a thousand knights."

Once again Arthur rowed out to return Excalibur into the stone anvil, and once again he brought it back to the lakeside.

" We will go to the holy church of St. Paul," decreed the Archbishop.

There he proclaimed Arthur king. The new

king knelt before the high altar, and placing his sword upon it to be blessed, he gave thanks to Almighty God, and the great and goodly company of brave knights cried :

"Arthur is our King ! Arthur is our King !"